PRISONER TO THE STREETS

Robyn Travis

Edited and published in the United Kingdom by:
OWN IT! Entertainment Ltd

Company Registeration Number: 09154978

Book Jacket Design: Ewan Green

First published by The X-Press 2013

WWW.OWNIT.LONDON

Since the First Edition of this book, we've lost many more young brothers and sisters.

I dedicate this New Edition to my young brother

Khiry Ford

A loving father and peaceful man taken way before his time.

The struggle continues...

I learnt the hard way that you can't be real in something that's fake and you don't need walls around you to be imprisoned.
This is the story of my life on Road.

ROBYN TRAVIS

THE CHASE

What the fuck have I got myself into? Again. This wasn't the first time in seventeen years that it crossed my mind as boi-dem chased us. I was having to ask myself that question on a weekly basis. If it wasn't one hype it was another. Robberies and drug running weren't really my thing but where beef was concerned you could bet your life on me.

A few of the brudders my age and older were goin' in and out of prison. I wasn't planning on joining them but it sounded like we were surrounded. Sirens from every direction, flashing blue lights everywhere. No time to watch that. Run first. Think later. Darker ran first. I followed. Boi-dem were only a long arm's length away when I breezed.

We were opposite McDonalds, on a back street off of Dalston Kingsland High Road, when boi-dem first clocked us. Like they'd been clocking us all summer. Like they always do in Holly Street and Hackney in general. They had been circling the area for weeks. As if something was going down. Something was going down, but nothing major. It was around midnight and we were just around the corner heading to Denisha' s yard. I was on my phone as Darker kneeled by a parked car. I could see he was up to sutt'n. He was either going to jack the whip or the stereo. I didn't really pay him no mind. Like I said, robbery wasn't really my ting. I continued chatting on the blower, minding my own business, until he was done with whatever he was doing.

I don't know where they came from but all of a sudden they were there. A police car, without its headlights on, pulled up right beside us. Then its sirens screamed.

Darker had already breezed by the time boi-dem jumped out and I was right behind, trying to catch up. Darker dusted down an alley that led into Kerridge, an estate on the border with Islington. That didn't trouble us. Hackney boys had no respect for Islington boys. It wasn't like they were going to argue about whose endz it was. They simply weren't on our level. Most of us Hackney boys were full of ourselves. The only surrounding area we had respect for was Totty. We didn't have much ratings for Leyton, Walthamstow or Stratford. Even though the African boys in E15 could fight, we were the heart of East London. And the hardest too.

Boi-dem didn't care about our rep. They didn't respect any of us. All they wanted to do was dash us in the bully van before their shift was done. They chased us like their livelihoods depended on it. I chased after Darker hoping he knew what he was doing.

The further he ran the more I lost faith. By now my lungs were burning like someone was sparking up a spliff in my chest. Every breath was a painful reminder that there was more at stake for me than TDA. I was fully strapped. And that would cost me more than a shit and a shave at Her Majesty's Pleasure. I kept on running.
By now I was fed up with the chase. I mean, I don't even run from my enemies. I couldn't understand how boi-dem had me shook. They weren't even strapped. Darker buss'd another corner, past the communal gardens and the football cage. Round the bend I dashed the gun into a bush. Fully loaded. Still running, I wondered if boi-dem had seen what I had thrown into the darkness. Man didn't have time to watch that. I had a £5 draw tucked in my socks but that was a minor, still.

Boi-dem were on to us differently. Refusing to give up. All that kept me going was the need to sleep in my own bed. At seventeen I'd already spent way too many nights sitting on a blue rubber mattress in a cell. Who knows how many times it's been pissed on. A warm bed and a spliff was all the motivation I needed to get home safe.

Man's freedom was always at risk, but the more we got away with it the cockier we became. Getting caught by boi-dem was a no-no. Bad bwoys ain't supposed to get caught. Especially black boys.

Me and Darker were easily up there amongst the fastest our age in Hackney, so we didn't have to worry about each other on a chase. We ran from police for fun on a regular. I was a big weed smoker back dem times so this chase was no joke ting. I was still boasy of my chances in a sprint with boi-dem, but I wasn't sure about going the distance before we ran out of road. I followed Darker, hoping he had a plan, but he turned right: wrong choice, we ran into a brick wall. Boi-dem were getting closer and closer. We were on our way to Feltham if we didn't make it over - FAST. Darker didn't hesitate until he had climbed to the top. Only when I reached there myself did I realise why. The wall we had climbed was nothing compared to the straight drop on the other side. It was like we were on the roof of a three or even four-storey house, staring down at the train tracks below. We looked at each other. The sound of heavy boots and walkie talkies focused our minds. We looked down again and I don' t know who said it, but all I remember hearing was "JUMP!"
Before I knew it, we were in mid-air and falling fast.

FREEDOM FROM THE WOMB

I was born prematurely at seven months. I wasn't expected to make it, but I did. Mum says I was a natural fighter from day one.
My first memory was of being on the platform at a tube station, wondering how the train came out of a wall. The noise it made was so loud I had to cover my ears. I remember a loud voice coming out of nowhere when the train stopped:

"MIND THE GAP! MIND THE GAP! MIND THE GAP!"

We boarded the train - me, mum and my brother. I was only two but I remember. It was a long journey. I've got a vague memory of saying 'Bye-bye' to a tall dark man when we reached our destination. I was more interested in staring out of a massive window with my brother, watching airplanes taking off. As I grew older I got to learn that the man at the airport was my biological father.

At three years old I started at Tiverton nursery, a short walk from home. It was in Tottenham in the borough of Haringey. I lived in a two-bedroom council flat on the Woodberry Down Estate on Seven Sisters which was technically in Hackney but a lot of the Woodberry Down boys saw themselves as 'Tottenham'.

Crazy to think that this little boy on his way to his first day at nursery would have to choose sides. A choice that would turn childhood friends into bitter enemies. In ten years the two boroughs would be at war, with bloodshed on both sides, giving police the excuse to put the community under surveillance and a lot of mandem under Operation Trident lockdown. Before that the only 'war' was 'Arsenal or Tottenham' coz the estate was halfway between the two football stadiums. Apart from that friends were just friends and postcodes didn't matter.

I went on to Tiverton Primary in the same building. It was multi-cultural but mainly African-Caribbean. In my class there were Somali, Turkish, Greek-Cypriot and Irish pupils. There was only one white English boy. My reception teacher, now Inclusion Manager at Tiverton, Rosemarie Palmer, said:

The Robyn I remember was a sunny, optimistic child. Physically slight, probably verging on skinny, and busy - always moving, probing, experimenting, experiencing life. He adored and admired his older brother and, regardless of the consequences, defended him to the hilt with 100% belief and commitment despite evidence to the contrary. I don't recall that he was outstanding academically, but he had an impact on the young teacher I was then and I remember him, despite all the decades in-between. I can still picture him; his head tilted reflecting on something I had said, digesting it, finding a place for my words in his world. If all my pupils over the years were likened to pebbles on the beach, Robyn's pebble would be the iridescent, distinctive, eye-catching, memorable pebble, and I have seen a lot of pebbles.

Tiverton was wicked. Most of my classmates were from the Tiverton Estate. Only me and one other boy were from Woodberry Down. I don't remember having a lot of fights or real arguments with anyone in those early school years.

I was good friends with most people. We used to play fight during break time, pretending to be WWF wrestlers and ninja turtles, but that was it. When we weren't elbow-dropping each other, we played football or raced across the playground. Nine times out of ten I was the winner. I always seemed to be ahead. Once I shot off like Linford there was no catching me.

My first set of real friends were from school - Roy, Pierre, Jermaine,

Od'z, Andrew, Blaze and Jason. We got on really well and became very close. Pure innocence at five years old. Yet six out of eight of us would end up in prison.

At six years old, school and life on Woodberry Down was my whole world. Me, mum and my brother were definitely the underprivileged on our estate. Some of our neighbours never let us forget it.

My brother was the best brother a boy could have - always funny, adventurous and a complete daredevil. But he was just too hype. I was his little follower and he was so many things to me - father, personal assistant, best friend and, at times, my worst enemy. So seriously did he take his roles that he never let me speak for myself. Mum would ask me if I was hungry. "No he's not," my brother would answer. She would cuss him off for not minding his own business. As a single parent, mum had to leave me and my brother alone in the flat when she was out making a living. Like I said, we were best of friends and at times the worst of enemies. When the enemy phase kicked in we fought like cat and dog. Especially after watching kung fu films.

My brother was three years older than me so I couldn't really test him physically. I had to be smart. If mum was home I got my punch in first and then screamed my head off, bringing her rushing into our bedroom just in time to see me being battered. She wasn't fooled by my antics, and used a belt, shoe or whatever she could find at close range to give us both some real good licks. As you can imagine, I didn't appreciate getting beaten up twice. Chups!
Mum didn't ramp when it came to licks. A curtain wire with a hook and eye at each end had me shitting myself. So did a belt called 'Johnny'. I never felt good when I saw my brother getting beats coz of me. Even if he had just punched me up. I guess I wasn't a fan of revenge, or a child who liked to see people suffer.

We watched *Desmond's* and *The Real McCoy*, two of the only black British shows on television in the '90s. My bedtime was usually before *The Real McCoy* and my brother's was soon after. Sometimes mum got so much joke from the show that she would forget to send me to bed. Dem times I got to watch the whole programme. I was too young to really understand the jokes but I got a great sense of pleasure from seeing my mum cry with laughter. It was better than hearing her cussing or seeing her stressed out, angry or upset.

One day I had came back from school and saw that Mum had this disturbed look on her face. I was five years old but I remember it clearly. She sat me and my brother down in the living room and turned off the telly. I studied her face, wondering what could be so important that she had to turn off *Desmond's*. Chups!
"Boys, I am really sorry to tell you this, but your dad won't be coming back." She softened her voice, and went straight to the point.

"He's dead."

My brother bawled with anger and began to wild out. My mother tried to calm him down as best she could. My heart skipped a beat. I got up and stood back, watching my brother's emotional outburst. He was definitely hurting; tears were flowing from my mother's eyes as she comforted him.

I felt hurt and confused. I was too young to remember the guy at the airport who left us a few years earlier. I was distressed at seeing my big brother freaking out like some kind of Tasmanian devil. It took mum ages to calm him down. They both looked devastated, their eyes red from all the tears. Mum called me over and gave me a hug. "You all right, son?"

"Yeah, mum."

The truth was I really wasn't, but I didn't want to show it. I struggled to understand my feelings. My hurt was not coz my dad was dead, but that my mum and my brother were hurting. Their pain and sorrow made me feel I had to be strong. I refused to let them see me cry.

I can't explain it, but even at that young age I knew there would be a big piece of a puzzle missing from my life which I would never get back. Things weren't great before dad died, but they got worse at home and at school. Me and my brother fought a lot more, or rather, I got beaten up much more. Mum seemed to be more hot-headed and would 'dish out' beatings like it was slavery times. She beat us any time she didn't want to hear our 'shit', as she put it. My brother seemed to be fighting every day. If it wasn't at school, it was on the estate. Everyone he fought was bigger and older. The kid had heart. Boys would come in numbers to fight him. He learned to win even when jumped on or rushed with surprise. He was a facety kid with a lot of mouth so he had to back up his talk. He learned to throw the first punch and run if he had to. These things were happening before dad died, but they seemed to get worse after.

Mum taught us from young that if one of us got into a fight we had to back each other to the end. It was a strict order. No exceptions to the rule. At school or on the estate, as long as we were together and one of us got into a fight, we were in it together. Without question, we had each other's back. I remember my first ever fight. I was five years old. I was playing football on the estate when one of the kids punched me. I walked upstairs to our flat on the first floor and went inside.

"Why's your face so push up?" mum asked.

"Malachi just hit me."

"And what did you do?"

"Nothing, mum. You hit me all the time."

Mum stood up. "Hear me good, I'm your mum," she said in a firm voice. "I gave birth to you. I didn't do that so that other people can beat you. Now go outside and don't come back until you win that fight. I'll be watching from the balcony."

I was shocked. Mum's giving me permission to fight. Rah! I went back downstairs with butterflies in my stomach. I was scared to start with but compared to how my brother whupped me, I couldn't see how this boy my age could cause me any real pain. In fact, I wiped the floor with him. I looked up. Mum seemed proud that I had defended myself. But I hated fighting. I would have preferred to let it slide without confrontation, but I knew if I didn't go and give Malachi a good hiding I would have to face Johnny at home. That day was a turning point.

Several people saw the new side to my behaviour and wondered what it was that caused "sweet little Robyn" to switch.

By Year 3 the change in my behaviour was evident. I went to school with a screwface most days and didn't pay attention in class. "Are you here today, Robyn?" Miss Leonard would say. The whole class would be giggling.

"Yes, Miss, I am here".

Mentally I was on a different planet.

Here's what what Miss Leonard said:

I remember Robyn well. A quiet, often sad boy. He rarely smiled and often came to school angry and frustrated about stuff that was happening at home. I encouraged him to take his anger out on a cushion or a teddy like a punch bag.

Robyn was underachieving although he appeared bright and eloquent. He looked thin and frail at times and appeared vulnerable. He rarely talked about issues at home but once told me he had to hide from people who banged on his front door trying to hurt his family.

Miss Leonard was a great teacher. For some reason she spent more time with me and my friend Andrew. She would take us aside and give us milk and other treats. She seemed really concerned as to why we looked so angry so early most mornings. I didn't look half as angry as Andrew did. There were tears in his eyes when he punched the teddy. That's how angry he was. He was also from a single parent family and his older brother used to beat him up and his mum didn't tolerate bullshit. Most mornings his face was just as shiny as mine. It must have been that petroleum jelly.

THROUGH A MOTHER'S EYES

In January 1987 my husband, the kids' father, went away for a so-called holiday. He wrote to his children continuously for a year, then the letters stopped. My older son blamed me for sending his dad away and Robyn soon followed. We had a love/hate relationship. When I beat my kids to discipline them it didn't always correct their bad behavior, but it made me feel a lot better. I had to gain some control so that they wouldn't walk all over me. I had to show them that I was the one who deserves their respect and I was in control.

The first year after my childrens' father went missing, I found a job in a nursery, hoping he would return to help lighten the financial burden. I also got more involved in an organisation called Hackney Black People's Association. I could finally express my feelings and issues as a black person in Britain.
In 1988 we had paid a visit to my Mum for a few weeks. When we returned to London it was obvious that someone had entered the flat while we were away. I found strands of a Caucasian person's hair on the bed. I also found broken glass in the sugar and in the rice.

Hackney Council had received a large amount of complaints from black residents about harassment at the time. Dog shit was posted through our letterbox on several occasions. And on one occasion a firebomb was thrown at the door charring most of it. Finally, we had a breakthrough. "NIGGA DIE" somebody shouted. I knew then for certain that it was racial harassment. My children grew so scared that on some nights I found them sleeping in the cupboard. I felt I had to be harsher on them to make them tougher. I didn't want them to be afraid of anything.

Later that year my mum moved down to London.

TRADING FEAR FOR FOOTBALL

It was a sunny day the last day of the summer term. The classroom buzzed with excitement as we settled down to watch the film, *The Lion King*. Twenty minutes into the action Simba's father was killed by his own brother. And then it finally hit me. My dad had been murdered. He must have been. He was too young to just drop down dead. Mum had told me two years earlier that my Grandad, her dad, had been killed in the States. He was shot in the head. No one ever spoke about it. Just like my dad's death. I couldn't watch the film any more.

A year passed. Tiverton was becoming a different place for me. I was eight years old and was now feeling like 'the man' in primary school. I had my little girlfriends and was good at the sport I loved - football.

It was play time. Me and my Year 4 friends were kicking a ball against a wall, playing a game called 'Wembley'. It was crap, I wanted to play a real football match. I went over to where the Year 6s were, "How about me and my friends play against your friends, we'll thrash yous lot anyway," I said.

The Year 6s laughed in my face so I kicked their ball over the fence. They went absolutely mad. Then one boy came up to me and gave me one hard push. He was much bigger than me. I went flying backwards. "Get off the pitch" he shouted. I felt uneasy with the familiar butterflies in my stomach. Then something happened.

"Your mum" I shouted.

He came up to my face "What did you say?"

I took a deep breath. "Your MUM."

"Your Mum", he screamed in my face. I pushed him back with little effect. He smiled, grabbed me, and said the wrong thing. Something that always started fights in the playground. "Your MUM, your DAD, the one you never had."

The boy and his friends started laughing. I took the bit about my dad very personal. I lost my temper to the point where I blacked out. The next thing I remember was being on top of this boy, throwing punches like my name was Mike Tyson. I was eventually pulled off by teachers and marched inside to stand outside the head teacher's office. Not for the first time neither. In fact, I was always outside the head teacher's office whenever anyone said, "Your DAD." It was my trigger button.

Year 5 had now arrived for me - my hairstyle was the lean. Similar to the mohican, but just on one side of the head. Like the singer Mark Morrison but with a plaited ponytail at the back. My face was still as greasy as ever with cocoa butter or Vaseline.

I was cool with the new Year 6s which meant my Year 5 boys could play on the main pitch every day. We loved it. Football was more important than playing 'kiss chase'. It was the only thing I cared about in school. The coach spotted my talents and made me captain of the school team - in Year 5! The team was mostly Year 6s. That's when it sunk in that I was good. But I was always fighting. Mr. Bucks, the coach, became very frustrated with me. "Robyn, you're a good boy. And we all know you're good at football, but you keep on fighting. Why?" I ignored him. "We're having a football competition next month at Arsenal football stadium. And I want you to play. But only if you promise to stay out of trouble until then." I was so excited I couldn't sit still.

"Yes, sir. Yes, sir. I promise I won't fight any more." Mr. Bucks left me with that promise.

One week into the promise and we had a new arrival in class. Our teacher Miss Griffith, a Trinidadian woman, introduced the new boy. Mohammed looked much older than the rest of us nine year olds. He had the face of an adult with hair on his chin and a slight moustache. And he was tall. Very tall. His veins were showing and, worryingly, he didn't look like he could smile even if he tried.

Mohammed was a Somalian with a strong accent. On his second day he asked "Who is the best fighter in the class?". He was like Schwarzenegger in Terminator, with a voice that was deeper than most of the male teachers in the school. Mohammed soon got the answer he was looking for: Jason, Od'z and Robyn.

One day me, Jermaine and Od'z were running jokes as usual. Miss had told us nuff times to be quiet but I was laughing the loudest. "Robyn, come out my class and don't come back in 'til you learn some manners," she shouted.

Cool, whatever. Standing on my own in the cloakroom outside was boring as hell. When she finally opened the door I thought I was going to get a lecture about 'my lack of manners'. But instead she was just kicking Mohammed out. I tried to ignore him but I couldn't. He kept trying to wind me up: "Robyn, your MUM." For the first time in my life someone said that and I didn't fight over it. I just ignored him; that's how much I wanted to play in that competition. But, he then said, "Hey you, your DAD."

"Don't say that. My dad is dead." Mohammed just held his stomach and laughed. The way he was laughing made my blood boil. I lost my temper and attacked this primary school Goliath with both fists flying and sent him crashing to the floor. He tried to fight back but, on that day, he was no contest.

Miss McArthur, the deputy head teacher, came running down the corridor and witnessed the scene at that exact moment. I tried to explain what had happened, but she wasn't having it. I was sent to wait outside the head teacher's office and my mum was called to the school. Again.

While I was waiting, Mr Bucks came and told me that I wouldn't be playing in the football competition the following week. I was heartbroken. Football was my life. I had messed up my dream of playing at Arsenal's stadium. Holding back my tears I begged Mr Bucks to give me another chance. "You need to learn how to control your temper," Mr Bucks shouted "Sorry. You can't play."

His mind was made up, no matter what I said. It was unfair. No one seemed to care. It didn't seem to matter that Mohammed had started it, I was going to be made to pay. I started hating Mr Bucks from that moment. But it didn't make things easier. I still had to face the next few days as my team mates prepared to go to Arsenal without me.

On the day of the competition I still hoped I would be given the chance to play. I went to school with my consent form and begged Mr Bucks once again, like my life was at stake.

"No. I have already made my mind up." This time, it really felt final. But, as Mr Bucks was talking with the head teacher who was wishing the team good luck, I saw my golden opportunity. I couldn't imagine the shame and embarrassment of having to return to class whilst the rest of the team was at Arsenal. Sneakily, I jumped over the school fence and ran to the back of the minibus. One of the boys let me in, I hid under the seats and Mr Bucks never saw me. The bus driver started the engine and we were on our way. I was happy. I was going to the Arsenal stadium and that's all that mattered.

We soon arrived at Highbury and I simply blended in with everybody else. We were finally inside the stadium. It was fantastic. I gazed at the past trophies. I admired the blown-up photos of Ian Wright, Paul Merson, Kevin Campbell and the other Arsenal legends. I stood there taking it all in, overwhelmed with excitement. Then I heard a familiar voice.

"Robyn, what on earth are you doing here?" Mr Bucks looked shocked and not amused.

"Sir, I had to come, this is my life, you don't understand." I wondered what would happen next. He was furious that I had tricked him.

"Right," he said. "The whole team has to go home because you didn't get permission to come." I showed him my forged consent form "You can watch, but you can't play," he said.

I was cool with the fact that I was allowed to stay and watch, but deep down I really wanted to play football so I could show off my skills. The competition was based on the FIFA World Cup model and there were school teams from all over London taking part. We lost the first match. It was frustrating watching my team do so badly. I begged sir to let me play. He refused. The second match ended in a draw. Mr. Bucks still didn't allow me to play. We had played two games and only had one point with one game remaining which we had to win in order to go through to the last sixteen which was the knockout stage. Suddenly Mr. Bucks tapped me on the shoulder and said "Robyn, go on the pitch and play, but you will still be punished when we return".

I was nervous but ready to play the match of my life. We started and went 1-0 down but then I scored soon after to make it 1-1. Then the other team scored and we went 2-1 down. Our subs tried to motivate us by singing a familiar song:

"2, 4, 6, 8 who do we appreciate - TIVERTON!"

Soon after that, Joe scored to make it 2-2 and we were back in business. There wasn't much time left and I was on the ball. One of the opposition went down in their area and the referee awarded a penalty to Tiverton. I was chosen to take it. There was thirty seconds or so left in the game. I was very nervous and I felt like the whole world was watching me. I placed the ball on the spot, took my run up and took my shot. For a split second my heart skipped a beat. The goal keeper went the wrong way and the ball was on its way in, then THUMP it hit the post. The ref blew the final whistle and it was all over.

I was heartbroken. I didn't care about getting into trouble or anything else in the world. I just felt as though I had let myself and my team mates down, and that if any football scouts were there looking for young talent, I had messed up my golden opportunity.

We moved to Holly Street Estate, Hackney in the winter of '95. There were nuff reasons why. It was just over a year since my mum was run over and almost killed by the National Front. Also, she wasn't coping very well financially. Sometimes there would be no food, gas or electricity in our flat in Woodberry Down. We would often have to walk from Seven Sisters to Dalston to Nan's place for that extra support. From N4 through N16 to E8. A couple of miles. That was a long arse walk as a kid. And it was always cold.

Mum had had enough and wanted a new life for us. Away from all the issues that we faced living in North London. When we first moved east I was still attending Tiverton School. Soon after my mum told me I would be going to London Fields Primary School for a week's trial. She said that if I didn't like it I could go back to Tiverton. I complained to her for the whole week that I hated it. After the week's trial my mum took me back to Tiverton. When we got there I noticed she had a big card in her hand. We went to my classroom and to my shock and disappointment my teacher announced that I was leaving. She told the class to sign the card.

--

I left some good friends behind in Tiverton but remained friends with Od'z, Jermaine and some others for a while. I would often travel the distance from Hackney to Tottenham to see them. However, at our age, it soon became a challenge for all of us to keep in contact. The distance was too far to maintain any real friendship, and we just drifted apart.

I started London Fields Primary School halfway through Year 5. It was very different and was a whole new experience for me. I had no friends at first which was strange, coz I was used to being the popular one. I wasn't going to beg to be friends with anyone doh, that's not what popular people do. So I just kept myself to myself and spent a lot of time alone.

After the first few weeks at London Fields, I woke up one morning and told my mum that I didn't want to go to school any more. She knew I hated it but I didn't let her know about some of the other things that were going on. I knew she would get angry and tell me to go and fight whoever was bothering me. There were times when I let people push or cuss me and I didn't retaliate. It wasn't coz I couldn't fight. It was coz I hated fighting. Plus, I had just left a school where I was known for fighting. I didn't want to have that rep at my new school. To go through these experiences and not fight back was really hard for me. I remember an occasion when some children in Year 6 threw stones at me on my way home from school. This upset me and I knew sooner or later I would have to fight back.

The playground was on the roof and only tennis balls were allowed. This had something to do with girls complaining about getting hit in their faces but also coz of the danger to passers-by of falling full-size footballs. As much as I hated it, playing football with tennis balls improved my skills. At break time one day, I was playing on my own when one of the boys from Year 6 called me over. "Yo, what's your name? You're wicked at football."

"Robyn."

"Robyn? Where's Batman?" I laughed thinking about the number of people who had used this same dead joke before. "Cool, my name is Jadie," he said.

"That sounds like a girl's name," I laughed "Were you named after your sister?"

We continued to run jokes for a minute. He invited me to come and play football with him and his friends. I was wearing my Arsenal shirt as usual and it turned out that Jadie was a hardcore football fan. Our great love for the game made us friends from day one.
Soon after I was in Year 6 which wasn't that bad, even though we used to bunk off school on the odd occasion. One time, me and some others called Kane and Derrick went walkabout during school hours. I was shocked to see Derrick picking up cigarette butts from the street and smoking what was left of them. Kane was the only other person who, like myself, wore hand-me-downs. His looked even worse than mine. Before I became friends with him, he and another

kid used to follow me from school but would always turn back before I reached home. God only knows why. Once they followed me all the way to my house. When I knocked the door, my mum opened and said "Aren't you going to let your friends in?"

"They're not my friends, mum." She thought I was joking so she told them to come inside and sent us to the shop to buy sweets and crisps. Kane and his friend smuggled their way into my life and got a packet of crisps out of it. Mum never had money to spend on me and my brother. So to spend the little money she had on boys I barely knew had me vex. But by the next day I saw the funny side to it and we became friends.

I was beginning to settle in at London Fields and was finding my way. Football was still my passion and I became the number one striker for the school. Just as I was getting into the swing of things, it was time for us to leave for secondary school. It was frustrating. I hated having to adapt to new surroundings.

It was now my second summer as a Holly Street resident. When I first moved there it was overcrowded with four tower blocks about 25 meters apart. Holly Street ran through the middle of the estate, surrounded by a few houses and a lot of other flats. I never really appreciated that we had moved from a council flat into a house. It was still on an estate and it wasn't fully ours. We had to share it with two other tenants. They rented a separate room each while my mum rented two rooms. One, a small box room, which me and my brother shared. There was no real privacy but there was a garden and that was great for me to practice my football skills.

I soon discovered that the area had a very bad rep. Me and my brother were riding our bikes through the flats late one summer evening not long after we moved in. We stopped to talk to one of my brother's friends by the lift. Two older boys appeared from nowhere and tried to stab my brother. They shouted and told him to get off his bike. I was shocked and scared. It was a revelation. Suddenly it dawned on me that the community spirit which was visible in the day was nowhere to be seen when it got dark. I was afraid of the environment that surrounded me. There was a certain energy in the air and I knew I had to toughen up and quick but, at the time didn't know how. I felt kind of defenseless.

My uncle came down a few weeks later and heard about what had happened. He was fuming. We jumped in his car and circled around the area looking for the boys. He saw some teenagers and grabbed them by their throats. I recognised one of them straight away to be the boy, but I said nothing and told him to let them go. My uncle's intentions were good, but at the same time hot-headed and stupid. He didn't think about the fact that me and my brother would have to deal with the consequences of his actions afterwards. I had already learnt about cause and effect at that young age.

After this, I saw a big change in my brother and there was a little in myself. We both knew that we didn't have much money and the bike that was stolen from my brother wasn't even his in the first place. My brother wanted money coz he was fed up of being broke. So he got us our first job delivering the Hackney Echo newspaper on the estate and Albion Square. Most kids in the area would have been too scared to deliver papers on that estate, especially on early winter nights but all we knew was that we needed the money bad. Fear could wait. Forget dem older Holly Street boys.

After I left London Fields Primary, I spent every day playing football. When it was really hot we had water fights and played a game called 40/40 with other kids. The estate was like the TV programme Eastenders. There was always some drama. My brother and his friends were always up to no good. Shooting pellet guns, climbing on roofs and being chased by the police. They would climb on top of the lifts in the tower blocks and somehow manage to control it and trap people inside. There wasn't much else on the estate for us to do.

My brother was concerned that I was too quiet and unsociable but knew I was really good with a ball. He took me to Saint Matthias Boys' Club on Dalston Lane where I joined the football team. I was happy coz now I had something to look forward to during the holiday weeks.

It was a warm summer's night, and my brother said "We're going out tonight." He gave me a look and I knew I just had to get ready. We walked the few minutes from Holly Street to London Fields where we met my brother's friend Aaron. Me and his brother Mannix were friends in school. Aaron was a mad one. He used to chase me and Mannix from their house into London Fields park around the corner for jokes.

Being out with my brother and Aaron had me acting up like I was some big man. It seemed like the right time for this to happen as I was due to start secondary after the summer holidays. We walked the back streets and ended up on Bethnal Green Road, outside an under 18s rave. I was only 11 years old. I didn't really listen to much music and wasn't really bothered about raving. I was just following the big boys.

We entered the club. My brother and Aaron seemed to be the cool guys, everyone seemed to know them. I was the smallest and youngest person in the dance by far. My brother and Aaron got on with it and left me alone. I was lost but happy at the same time. There were nuff older girls smiling at me. My brother and his bredrins made me dance with an older girl and things took off from there. It was nuff jokes. Everyone was hyping me up coz I was this little kid whining up my little waist with this teenage girl. I felt like THE MAN.

I heard all sorts of new music that night. Jungle, House, Garage, Reggae, Bashment and a few other songs that I already knew. The rave scene was a totally new experience for me and I had a wicked time. Walking home afterwards I felt like the character called Kid from the film *House Party*. This was one of the best days of my summer holiday but, just like Kid, I had to now explain to my mum what I was I was doing out at that time of the night. The thought of getting beats didn't take away from the fun I had doh.

I started secondary in September '96. It was a Roman Catholic school called St Richards but there was nothing holy about the place. Settling in at St Richards wasn't really hard - my brother already went there. I had two main friends D-Lowe and Anthony. I knew Anthony from St Matthias. D-Lowe was the younger bro of my brother's friend, Big D-Lowe.

Being the younger brother of someone in school had its advantages. Nice girls in the older years would hug and kiss us and say, "Aww, look at little D-Lowe and little Travis, they're so cute". Also, older boys didn't mess with you once they found out who your bigger brothers were. I never called on my brother to fight my battles though. It wasn't the manly thing to do. If you had a big mouth when getting into beef then called your brother to fight your battles, you weren't serious.

But then there were the disadvantages. Teachers were constantly watching you, waiting for you to slip up. The names Travis and Lowe had a bad rep in that school way before me and little D-Lowe got there. St Richards had nuff gangs - NF boys, triads, and crews from North, East and West London. And, secondary school was just like primary - I managed to get myself into scraps all the time.

Within a few months of settling into St Richard's, we got the news that the school would be closing down at the end of the year. I was furious. The next school would be my fourth in four years. Coz me and D-Lowe didn't want to be separated, we asked our mums to apply for the same schools. They applied to many schools but all the Year 7s were full already. We finally got accepted at St David's and St Katharine's aka D&K [now Grieg City Academy] in Haringey.

My first impression was a good one; The football pitch was much better than St Richard's and the uniform was better. Except the blazers. My blazer almost reached my kneecaps. D&K was another Roman Catholic school with nothing holy or Catholic about it.

LIFE BETWEEN D&K AND HOLLY ST

D&K had a tough reputation. I promised myself that if anyone tried it on me I would nip it in the bud. I didn't want to fight but I was willing to take on anyone regardless of age, size or reputation. The Robyn my mum and brother had wanted me to be, was now ready to defend himself. No one was going to put their hands on me without a good fight. No one.

Our first day at our new school was the third Monday in February, just after the half-term holidays. D&K was much bigger and had all its buildings on the same site, so all of the year groups shared the same space. Me and D-Lowe were in the reception area waiting to be placed in our form classes. Two beautiful girls walked past and smiled at us. Me and D-Lowe gave each other a cheeky high five. We knew we would be happy at D&K.

I was taking in the vibe of the school. At break time I couldn't help but notice that there were so many black kids and so few white kids. In the playground I locked eyes with this one guy. "Nah, no way, it can't be. What you doing in my school, bruv?" It was my good friend Od'z from Tiverton. We both started laughing. It had been four years since we last linked. We were twelve years old now and had grown a lot. There were a few more familiar faces in the playground. We greeted each other and I introduced them to D-Lowe.

Geezer, one of my friends from E8, came over. I was in my element. My group of friends included boys from Hackney, Tottenham, Wood Green, and a few from Hornsey. There were 15-20 of us and we were definitely the most popular boys in our year.

At first no one wanted to take my brother into their school, but eventually months later he joined me at D&K. He had made quite a name for himself and was well known in and out of Hackney. His negative rep followed him like a shadow. At St Richard's he was a terror and made life difficult for students and staff alike. In D&K he was a 'gyalist', and even though he spoke to a few of the Tottenham boys that he grew up with he never really mixed with them. He was very much his own person. Like me, my brother had lost contact with many of his childhood friends from Tottenham. Now we were back in a school dominated by people from there.

One morning, towards the end of May '97, I was I staring out the window in a French lesson when I saw some of the older boys from Year 10 and 11 crying whilst hugging a girl from Year 9. I was curious to find out why they were so upset. When I returned home my brother told me that some Hackney boys, a little older than himself, had just killed a sixteen year old boy from Tottenham called Popcorn. A few months earlier, I was told, a sixteen year old boy called Guydance from Hackney was shot and killed. According to the media the killing of Popcorn was a revenge attack. These two murders generated nuff hate between Hackney boys and Tottenham boys, and yet they were unrelated. The media played a big part in creating the illusion that there was some connection between them.

Judging by the reaction of D&K's older pupils from North, Popcorn was a well-known and well-loved figure. They were saddened by his murder and found it hard to deal with. There was definitely something in the air. At school I noticed that a few of the older Hackney boys didn't want to be associated with Hackney. Some of the older boys from Tottenham, Wood Green and Finsbury Park began throwing their weight around anyone who wasn't from their area. But they were also wary about who they tested. Me and the Year 7 boys from Hackney and Tottenham felt the vibe but we were too young to get involved. It was none of our business.

The Holly street transition was nearly complete. Tower-blocks were knocked down, residents were promised a better life with less grime, children on the estate were promised the use of nearby Queensbridge Leisure Centre for football and other sports. But the heart of the community had been ripped out. Our lives had been disrupted far longer than we expected and whilst some residents began to move back in, many people got fed up of waiting on the new flats and took offers to be re-housed elsewhere. Our estate, as a community, broke down. 'Til today, a lot of us believe the real reason the estate was demolished was that the police didn't feel safe there and wanted to 'divide and conquer' the community.

I was still playing football for Saint Matthias Boys' Club. Our coach said some professional football scouts would be coming to watch us play in a few weeks. "Be ready to impress. This may be your big chance," he said. I was already well prepared apart from one thing. Money was always tight at home but I wouldn't ask my mum for something unless I really needed it. This time I really needed a pair of football boots, to impress the scouts. I asked, but Mum didn't have the money. She told me to ask my aunts and uncles to help out but I knew they would only help if I stayed out of trouble. As I was on suspension, I didn't bother.

'Til I was thirteen I'd never worn name brand. The choice of trainers in my price range were Dunlop, Gola, Nicks, Ascot, Kingfisher and Plimsoll. Hi-Tee if you're lucky. That was it. Plimsolls meant you had it really hard. I didn't care about name brands but I felt the pressure to fit in and have the Nike and Adidas my friends had. Especially if someone tried to run jokes on me by saying, "Rob, you got ripped off. Dem Nikes are spelt wrong." In other words, my Nicks were shit. I became self-conscious, programmed into thinking I needed these things to be accepted. That same summer me and Porkpie were riding our BMX bikes when a car on Dalston Lane sped up as we were crossing - then BANG! I fell in the road. The driver didn't realise he had hit me and that the car was resting on my foot.

My foot was severely fractured. The doctor said it would take six months to heal and a further three months to get back to normal. He stressed how important it was for me to rest my foot. That was when it hit me that I wouldn't be able to play football for months. My heart was broken and my dreams shattered. I would miss the opportunity to impress the football scouts who were coming to watch us the following week. I held back the tears. My mum knew football was my life: "Never mind, son, you'll be back."

I could barely move for the first month. By the time I started to walk again it was September and I was back at school, in Year 8, after my suspension. Not even three weeks later and I managed to get myself suspended again. I can't remember what triggered this one. I can only assume that some boy had cussed me about my trainers or cussed my dad and people were laughing and it caused me to switch. The only explanation I can give for breaking his glasses is that he was a year younger. I guess I didn't want to physically hurt him so I did what I thought was the next best thing.

The end of September and I had just come off suspension. I was two months into my six-month recovery. It was time for Year 8 football trials. I didn't tell the Coach about my injury. I turned up at the trials with a packet of painkillers. I took four and started to play. I couldn't believe how shit I was. I couldn't run as fast and my ball control was poor. I couldn't shoot with my right foot, my main foot, the foot that got run over. The pain was just too much. When the trial was over Mr Bomaker said he was impressed and that I had made the team. I was still in a lot of pain but I was happy. On the way home I took two more pain killers. Our first match was not until October so at least I had a little time to rest my injured foot.

HACKNEY v TOTTY, NOT OUR BUSINESS

In Year 8 my bredrins were pretty much the same as they were in Year 7. There was me, Geezer, Pork Pie, D-Lowe, Evil Kid, Danny Boy and Ash-Man, who was in the year below. We were all from Hackney. Then there was Gabs, Bucks, Od'z , Millz, Marcellus and a few others who were from Tottenham. Bagzy and Fari were from Wood Green. We knew we were top boys in our school. We would link up at break-time and lunch time. Some to play football and others to smoke weed. But one thing that everyone was there for was to run jokes.

After school we'd go to Wood Green to play video games and look gyal. Then back to Tiverton to chill. If there were any under 18s raves at the weekend we would link up and go. Either to Ally Pally or to a rave called Exposure in Wood Green. Many of the Tottenham and Edmonton boys would be there. You could count the Hackney boys at the rave on one hand. We'd also rave in Tottenham at venues like Pleasure Rooms and Temple. This was the time that the jungle scene was coming to an end. MCs like Skibadee, Shabba and Det, were mashing up the dance scene. Jungle tunes like Helicopter and Wolf would set da mandem in the dance on a different hype. Although we were from different areas it never got in the way of our friendship. I considered this group to be my real friends, even though we didn't have a lot in common. I wasn't interested in the smoking and I wasn't as loud as some of the others. But I still felt comfortable with my mandem.

It was six months since Popcorn's death. At school, me and my boys would wind each other up. Those who lived in Tottenham would say,

"What are you Hackney boys doing in our Tottenham man school?" Then us who lived in Hackney would reply, "What? Hackney man run D&K." After these exchanges of words, play fights would kick off. We would play fight so viciously we ended up beating each other up. Sometimes in class the Tottenham boys would threaten to jump me because I was outnumbered. I would then pick up a chair and a compass and say, "If you lot try to rush me, I swear I will lick you down with this chair and jook you with this needle."

To us it was just a game, and we never took it seriously. Sometimes the Tottenham boys would get a flying kick in the back, and a severe beat down in the playground if we caught them slipping, and vice versa. It was just fun and games.

At the end of the school day we would all jump on the 144 bus to the top of Wood Green and pop style. Most of us D&K boys were like celebrities to a lot of the girls from surrounding schools in the area. At this time in my life I was as broke as a joke. My mum used to give me £5.00 a week for pocket money and that meant I had £1.00 a day to spend. I wasn't mad at her. I knew she didn't have it. Some of that would have to get used on bus fare or man would just make a fake bus pass. I was never the envious type. Sometimes after school I would be with da mandem in Wood Green and have to stand and watch certain man go into Footlocker on a Monday and say, "I'm buying this pair of trainers blud". By Wednesday they'd be wearing their new pair of trainers to school.

I had to accept that I wasn't as lucky as some of these small foot man. At thirteen I was wearing size seven shoes, which meant adult price trainers. Like I said, I wasn't the envious type, but sometimes I wished my feet were smaller.

From Footlocker we'd cross the road and go into the arcade to play a racing game called Daytona. It was the only reason we went into Sega Park. It was the best game in there. Six of us could play at the same time. 50p per game. As much as I wanted to play, no way was I going to spend a big 50p just to fit in with the rest of da mandem. My mum's £5.00 wasn't even guaranteed every week so more time I acted like I wasn't in the mood to play.

We would then bop to the top of Wood Green to catch the 67. This bus took us through Totty to Dalston in Hackney. Everyone loved this bus journey after school. You were guaranteed nothing but jokes, girls, and very often a good rockers.

On one of these journeys I was not my usual self. I was extremely quiet and wasn't in the mood for running jokes. I got lost in my own thoughts, trying to think of ways to make money without hurting anyone. Enough was enough. I was fed up of being broke. I remembered that two years earlier my brother was working in a chip shop in Dalston. It looked like this chip shop was paying some good money. He was wearing a lot of designer clothes and name brand trainers. My brother didn't seem to complain about not getting pocket money. When he left the job he was still looking fresh to death. He was making some sort of money, but I never knew how.

That night after school I came home and thought more deeply about how my brother was able to buy dem flash things. He was barely sixteen years old and didn't have a job. Yet he owned a big gold chaps, an Avirex jacket, a widescreen TV and a stereo system. What made me more curious was the way his whole bedroom was kitted out. I also thought of the times when there was no food in the house and my brother would give mum some change and even buy us a takeaway from the Chinese. His flash mobile never stopped ringing. Whenever he answered it he would say, "How much do you want?" Or sometimes, "What you looking for? I got the ting." Or, "I ain't got nothing, I'm dead right now, phone me later and I'll be live."

I finally asked him how he was making money. He confirmed my suspicions that he was a dream chaser. Later that night his phone rang, and he left in a hurry. When my brother left I went into his room and took some of his see-through packets. I then went into my mum's cupboard in the kitchen and took out a container full of her herbs and spices. I searched for the one that looked just like weed and placed it evenly into a few packets. I went to school the next morning looking for some clientele for my new business as a herb dealer. I sold packets of mixed herbs & spices to some Asian boys who had just started to smoke weed.

My biggest client was one rich Asian boy called Marvin. I made enough money off him and the rest of his weed smoking friends to last the week. I wasn't greedy. I only sold like three £10 packets a week. Marvin was always smiling and claimed that he was high, so I continued to sell it to him. This hustle didn't last too long as my bredrins mouths were too loud. When Marvin said, "Yeaah, Robyn's got some good shit, man," everyone cried with laughter. Then one of my bredrins said, "Nah bruv, dat ain't good shit, it's bullshit. You're smoking kitchen herbs, bruv."

In a split second my hustle was over. Just like that. I wasn't even angry about it. Actually I found it funny, until I was broke again a week or two later. Meanwhile, my brother was in year 11 getting it in. He had just recently bought a brand New Typhoon moped straight out of the showroom. Watching his lifestyle had me really tempted to chase dreams myself. It wasn't the title I was after, because I had already witnessed the beef which followed my brother because of that kind of hustle. For me, it was just about being able to afford the stuff I needed and wanted, without having to beg no-one for nothing. I just wanted to have money in my pocket.

So I approached my brother one evening and told him I wanted to chase dreams or whatever else he was doing. He gave me a serious look and said, "Nah bruv, I don't want that for you. Focus on your school work and football. You're gonna make it big one day. Trust me". I was mad that he wouldn't let me chase dreams with him, but I could see he was trying to protect me from sutt'n. I had respect for him, so I listened. My brother always tried to guide me in the right way and to shield me from the lifestyle of the street. He could see I wasn't cut out for it.

Regardless of what he wanted for me, I was still getting into fights. Two or three times a day.

BROTHERLY LOVE

Coz of the long distance, to get to school on time most mornings I missed out on breakfast. Tiredness and hunger put me in a bad mood. Sometimes I was so hungry and tired I couldn't focus in class. All I could do was daydream. Then I'd have to deal with a teacher shouting at me coz I'd dozed off during a lesson.

One afternoon I was sent out of the lesson for sleeping. Out in the corridor I started to think about the reasons why I always got kicked out of class. When it wasn't for sleeping it was for running jokes or fighting. As I leaned against the wall I noticed some year 11 boys play fighting. They were the Tottenham boys who were seen as the main guys in the school at that time. Being only thirteen I never really cared about street life or who was who. They looked over towards me. My eyes locked with one of them, a well known Totty boy called Marley Maximus. He screwed his face and said, "What you looking at? Move from round here likkle bwoy."

I kissed my teeth. Is this guy stupid or what? I'm outside my lesson. Where am I meant to go? He came closer. "Move. Move," he shouted. He grabbed me. So I grabbed him back. We held on to each other but he was older and much stronger than me. He pulled me round the corner where a crowd gathered and watched me being dragged like a rag doll. It was time to fight. The fact that he was older didn't mean I was scared of him. I was good to go.

Out of nowhere, my brother came running through the crowd . "Let go of him now," he said. My brother was vex. He took off his jacket and the rings on his fingers and gave them to me to hold. He told Marley Maximus and his six foot friend to come around the corner and fight. The whole school wanted to follow but my brother and Marley Maximus told them to stay and for some reason they all listened.

Shit! I'm about to start this Hackney/Totty thing for real now. What have I done?

Round the corner it seemed that Marley Maximus didn't want to fight. He paced up and down nervously. "Gimme a minute," he told my brother. "I gotta go to the classroom to get something out of my bag."

I looked at my brother. "That's dodgy," I said. "Maybe he's got a borer in his bag."

"Don't worry," my brother said. "I've got one in my bag, and my bag's in the same classroom."

As they walked towards the classroom I overheard Marley Maximus saying, "If I knew he was your likkle brother I wouldn't have dragged him up like that."

"That's cool," my brother responded. "But don't make that mistake and touch him again." To my surprise, that was the end of the drama.

But, a similar situation happened a few months later. This time with a boy called Darrel. He grabbed me so I grabbed him back. Once again, he was older, stronger and much taller than me. Soon after lunch registration I saw my brother in the corridor. He was fuming. "Who did it? Who did it?" "Did what?" I was confused until I realised what he was talking about.

"Oh, it's nothing big. We were just grabbing each other. The boy Darrel was just showing off himself coz girls was about."

"What does he look like?" At that moment Darrel walked past. So I pointed him out. My brother walked up to him very calmly.

"Why did you put your hands on my little brother?" Darrel screwed up his face and smiled, all the time looking down at my brother. What happened next surprised even me. My brother jumped up and head-butted Darrel, followed by a knee in the face as Darrel doubled with pain. Then a punch and a sweep of the legs, which brought Darrel to the ground. Hard. He kicked Darrel like a football. I tried my best to stop my brother and save Darrel but it all happened too quickly. Darrell was taken to hospital and put in intensive care.

My brother was permanently expelled. Immediately. He didn't look too bothered about it. I was angry and frustrated that my brother got chucked out of school coz of me. The teachers didn't bother to find out what actually happened. If they had bothered to ask, they would have found out that Darrel started it earlier in the corridor with me.

It's funny how some teachers forget that there are two sides to every story. Darrel was made to look like the victim, which, in my opinion, wasn't the whole truth.

Months later my brother was told that he would be allowed back in school to take his GCSE exams. He was told this at such short notice that he didn't have enough time to prepare. So he failed them. Joke school system. Chups!

Seven months into the recovery period after my accident, the D&K football team reached the finals of the Haringey Cup. I was haunted by the fear that I may never get my form back. I was worried that my one dream of becoming a famous footballer would be just a dream and that the accident had ruined my life. I wasn't half the player I used to be but I was still one of the best strikers in the team.

We met Gladesmore School in the cup final at their ground in Tottenham. Our team was always cocky coz most of our players were being offered trials for professional teams. We felt that we could win by just showing up. So we didn't bother to put in the effort. We played the game in our usual style - slow to begin with. When we eventually decided to take the game seriously, we won easily - 3-1 - to become Haringey champions for the 97/ 98 season. I scored two headers and another boy scored an amazing free kick.

A week later I was told I'd been selected for Haringey Borough team. I doubted the level of my skills after the accident, but I was happy that people still had faith in me. Mr. Bomaker told me I could only play if I stayed out of trouble. I kissed my teeth. Not again! Why did teachers always use the one thing I loved as a weapon against me? They knew I was better at football than anything else. What was the point of punishing me with it? Other than football, maths was a subject that I seemed to be doing well in. For some reason, it went unrecognised when me and some of the other so-called badly behaved boys made it into the top group. "Why are you and Gabs in our class? You lost?" some of the girls laughed. "This is the top group, y'know." I laughed coz they were only joking, but I wondered why teachers rarely gave us praise for certain achievements. It's hard to believe in yourself when there's little encouragement. It always felt like my negative actions got me more attention than my positive ones.

SUMMER OF CRAZY HYPE

Year 8 had now ended. The summer that followed was a mixture of fun and crazy hype. I was still playing football but spent most of my time hanging with the Holly Street boys on the estate late into the nights. As it was summer, the rave scene was popping with a lot of under 18s shubz. Sometimes me, Geezer and the other boys from Holly Street would rave at Cheeky Bees, our weekly spot in Hackney. Any time we herd there was a shubz in the endz we would gatecrash it. Then there were the raves which you couldn't miss if you wanted to feel like you were somebody big. Raves where the Heartless Crew used to mc and deejay. They mainly played Garage along with Bashment, RnB and a touch Jungle.

For most kids summer was about having fun but, on my estate that fun was always interrupted by some of drama. This is Holly Street.

One day I was in the front room chatting with my Mum trying to convince her that I needed a mobile when the house phone rang. From the look on her face the call caused her heart to race. She slammed down the phone, reached for her jumper and ran out the door half-dressed. I followed. It had to be something serious. She ran rounder the corner to Beechwood Road. There was my brother surrounded by nuff plain clothes officers, a police car on either side with lights flashing. "Why are you grabbing up my son?"

"We are going to arrest him" an officer replied.

She demanded their IDs as they weren't wearing uniform. They ignored her. So she stood between them and my brother. The officers called for back-up. People from the estate started gathering, concerned at the way boi-dem were handling my brother. The officers than made a big mistake. They tried to manhandle my mum. Instantly me and my brother switched.

Suddenly we were in a wrestling match with boi-dem. My mum and brother seemed to be handling them, whereas my thirteen year old frame was held down hard on the bonnet of a car. One of the boi-dem used the opportunity to slam sneaky punches in my rib cage. By the time back-up came, the crowd had started to cuss off the police for their violent behaviour.

My mum and brother were arrested and put in the bully van. Boi-dem finally let go of me and I made my way home. Some older girls from the area helped me push my brother's brand new moped back to my house. I felt useless. If only my dad was alive, boi-dem wouldn't have been able to do my mum like that.

This was my first beating from the police, and I wasn't even thirteen.

When I got home my mum's so-called boyfriend was there. This wutless man was a Trinidadian called Junior who, for some reason, could not bend his left leg. I used to see him in church, then he started coming to the prayer meetings my mum used to have in our flat. A year after moving to Holly Street my mum took me on a prison visit to see this prat. I was confused; he wasn't my dad and I didn't give a damn about him. The next time I saw him he turned up at our door with a see-through bag marked H.M.P. I soon realised he had come to live in our house. I then figured out why he was staying in mum's room. I stared at him wondering why he didn't do fuck all to help us.

The only thing that this man did was run down the road to tell my Nan about what had happened. It was a silly thing to do. He knew Nan had a serious heart condition. News like that could have caused her to have a serious heart attack. I was so vex with him but I stayed calm. I could've switched and stabbed him at that moment.
I started to think about the kind of person he was and all the things

he used to do when he first moved into ours. He had been in prison for stabbing his wife in the neck, in front of the kids. He was always trying to feel up my mum in front of me, to her disapproval. I wasn't one of those kids who would sit and watch that disrespectful shit. I was ready to switch on him many times coz of it. He also let his son come round and play the new Playstation but wouldn't let me join in. All I could do was sit and watch. What's worse, he was only able to get the Playstation from the catalogue in my mum's name. I was older now and angrier. I wanted to do him same way he did his wife. I was also angry at my mum. She should never have let Junior move in.

They were back from the police station and there was a lot of bitterness in the air. Later that night my brother attacked Junior. I don't know why he did it. I guess he was as angry as I was about this man living with us.

My brother told me about the mix-up with the boi-dem. They claimed he had drugs in his possession and chucked them away when he saw them. But they never pressed charges. The next day they came round and asked mum if she wanted to make a complaint about police brutality. She said she didn't want to because she was fearful that her boys would be targeted by the police.

A few weeks later Junior was kicked out the house. It had been brewing for a while and the time for him to go had come.

The summer holiday of '98 was coming to a close and the crazy hype was still competing with the fun. Late one night I was sitting with my mum and she told me to take the rubbish out. As I got to the rubbish skip downstairs, I heard a voice shouting. "Shoot me!"

I looked around and saw my brother with his friend Bola. One of the older guys from around the area called Beefy, who had recently become a crack head, was pointing a gun at my brother's head, then at Bola's head, then back to my brother.
I dropped the rubbish and breezed over. By this time my brother was enraged and had lost his mind. "Shoot me then, bruv," he continued to shout. This madness eventually calmed down when some of Beefy's friends pulled him away with my brother and Bola shouting

and calling him a pussyhole.

I looked around. People older than myself seemed shaken by what had happened. I felt scared for my brother. Through this fear and anger, I made a mental note of everyone who had ever messed with us. When I get older, I'll deal with them myself.

That revenge list was growing quicker than I was. I spent the rest of the summer holiday riding around the estate on my brother's 'ped'. I was one of the few boys my age who knew how to ride one.
It felt good that my brother was making money. Many times when we had no food, electricity or heating, he would use his earnings to lighten the burden. In my eyes that made him the man of the house. It was almost time for me to go back to school and I was worried that I would be wearing the same old holey trainers. My mum was still struggling to provide for me.

Aunty Jay came up to visit and must have seen our struggle. She took me out and bought me two pairs of Nike trainers and some school shoes as an early birthday present. I was very pleased and content at my third pair of name brand trainers ever.

Having Aunty Jay around exposed me to a different kind of lifestyle. She lived in Surrey. Another world from Hackney and Tottenham. More spacious and green. Even the air smelt cleaner. When we visited she would take us out to restaurants - a new experience for me. I got to try food outside that wasn't eaten out of a box.

Aunty Jay even took me to my first football match in 93 at Highbury. She also paid for my friend Jermaine to join me. There were times when my other Auntys took time to help us with our school work and I respect them for the effort they put in. But it was the experience with Aunty Jay that opened my eyes to a whole new way living. When I was with her time seemed to slow down. I learned that whatever I want, if I work hard enough I can get.

My family had high hopes for me from a young age. I knew what my Aunty had was achievable. But I had a very bad temper which could prevent me achieving.

TEMPER, TEMPER!

The summer holiday was finally over and I returned to school. In Year 9, I was caught between two different personalities; 'sweet bwoy' and 'hot-head'. If I had to choose I would have gone for the sweet bwoy but I couldn't shake off the demons of anger and frustration.

A few weeks later I managed to get myself suspended from school. Again. Even though my mum always had my back she got fed up with the teachers calling her to the school every five minutes. The teachers warned me that if I got into a fight or any sort of trouble again, I would be expelled for good. No more excuses. I was given a mentor, an old lady called Mrs Lumb. She told me to take deep breaths when I was angry. If you ask me, she needed mentoring.

One morning, I was lining up outside assembly with the whole of Year 9. Fed up of always being in trouble, I kept myself to myself . My friends were fooling around and running. As I watched, I felt a thump on my head. I looked over and saw my Jamaican friend Ricky swinging his boot bag and smiling. I took deep breaths, like Mrs Lumb said, but that shit didn't work. So I ran up to Ricky and gave him a soft punch in the back to even things up.

I got back in line with my class. A moment later, I felt a blow to the side of my face. It was Ricky again. He was holding on to my shirt, cussing in patois, asking why I had boxed him. "Ah wha' de bloodclaat you ah do, Robyn. Wha' you ah do? WHA YOU AH DO?"

I tried to calm down and talk Ricky out of it. "Ricky, y'know I'm on my last chance. I don't wanna get expelled. Let's forget this ever happened." My classmates couldn't believe I was trying to talk my way out of the beef. But eventually I couldn't hold down the demons of my ego and temper. Ricky let go of my shirt and as he did, I switched. I punched him in the face and continued punching until I finally ended up on top of him. Teachers came bursting through and dragged me off Ricky.

I couldn't understand how I got involved in the first place. Ricky was my bredrin. We never had a problem before. As we were writing our statements, Ricky turned to me and asked, "Why did you punch me in the back?"

"You started it," I replied. "You hit me with your boot bag, and you don't even play football, bruv."

"Robyn, you're crazy, I didn't even know I hit you. It must have been an accident." We both laughed. He told me not to worry coz he would take the blame for what had happened. I respected him for that and the teachers gave me the benefit of the doubt.

A few weeks after, I was on the 144 going to school and was running ten minutes late. On the journey I overheard a boy called Joel, in Year 10, bragging to some year 11s that he and his friends jumped a boy I knew from Hackney called Danny Boy. I remembered hearing earlier in the week that Danny Boy had been in a bad way. He wasn't my close friend but he was cool with some of da mandem.

When I heard this boy laughing I felt I had to say sutt'n. "Oi, 'llow dem talk, Danny's my people." He smiled and kept boasting. "Blud, if I hear one more word about Danny come out your mout', it's on," I said. He carried on chatting rubbish. I flung my head back, kissed my teeth and stared out the bus window.

Rah, here we go again. Why does everybody think they're a bad bwoy? I tried chat to this prick nicely. He's taking me for a dickhead. He must think I'm a pussy. Fuck it. It's on. When the bus stopped I dashed my school bag to the ground and stepped to him. I sparked him straight in the face. No long ting. He fell down then got up, holding his bloody nose and ran off down the road. The Year 11s seemed shocked.

"Rah, this younger can rock," I heard someone say. I can't even lie. I was gassed up when I heard that. It had me believing in my own hype. But the high of the hype quickly faded when I clocked that I would have to face the consequences of my actions.

I sat in the first lesson that day thinking, if I make it to lunchtime without being questioned about the fight there's a good chance the teachers don't know about it. Moments later, I heard a knock on the classroom door. The deputy head walked in. I tried to play it cool but I knew he had come for me. The whole class knew. He called my name and told me to follow him to the head teacher's office and to bring my bag and coat. My heart sank. I had a feeling this would be my last lesson at D&K. I sat outside the office pretending to be confused about why I was there. I tried my best to front. The look on the deputy head's face was like - Whatever! While I was waiting, a tall black man approached. "Are you Robyn?"

"Yes," I replied.

"You're the young man who broke my son's nose?"

"Yeah."

"So tell me what happened."

I told him that his son was bragging about beating up one of my people, so I switched on him. I thought Joel's dad was gonna do the hard man ting and threaten me. Instead he asked the head teacher not to punish me. He also asked me to promise him that it was over between me and his son. So I did. Then I was sent back to my class.

I had a lot of respect for Joel's dad. It meant a lot to me that, as a black man, he didn't want me expelled. During break-time it seemed like everybody was coming up to me to ask about the fight. I didn't want to stir things up or sound like I was bragging about the situation. I had made a promise to Joel's dad, and I wasn't going to break it. When anyone asked, I would just say, "Whatever you heard happened is what happened. It's nutt'n to talk about."

At lunch time I heard that a boy called Smithy had grabbed up my friend Ash-Man to do with the fight between me and Joel. Smithy was Joel's best friend. Smithy had overheard Ash-Man talking about the fight and told him to shut up and stop talking about his best friend, Joel. Ash-Man said he told Smithy that I was his friend and Smithy replied, "So what. I'm not scared of Robyn; my name ain't Joel". When I heard this, I took it as a diss straight away. It was like he was saying that he could beat me up. My ego couldn't handle it. I had to save face.

At 3:30 when school was done I looked for Ash-Man and asked him to show me this Smithy brudder. We walked to the 41 bus stop where he was waiting with friends. "Wha gwarn, bad man?" I said. "Why are you putting your hand on my likkle bredrin Ash-Man?"

He screwed up his face. "I'm not Joel, you know." I responded with a couple of hard punches to his face. Then some of my bredrins started to attack him. But some big-boned girls who were his friends got involved and shouted that we should leave him alone.

True say they were girls we just thought, ah 'llow it. I was frustrated it ended that way. I didn't want my friends to get involved. Still, I felt that Smithy got the message. Me and my friends jumped on the bus and headed towards Wood Green. When we got to there our usual group of ten to fifteen boys from Hackney and Tottenham was much smaller. There were only six of us. Evil Kid and some others went to Footlocker to look at some crep. While me and Od'z went to Sega Park across the road to check out the girls as usual. We were chilling when I saw Smithy walking towards us with two older boys - around 18-19 years old - either side of him.

Smithy's whole body language was much more aggressive than earlier. Now he had back-up he was acting like a real bad bwoy. The two older boys quickly grabbed my arms so couldn't move. Smithy punched me a couple of times with a knuckle duster. Od'z switched and attacked the older boys. In an instant, my hands were free. I was like a dog being let off its leash. I charged at Smithy and started to punch his face off.

The fight was broken up by the Sega Park staff. Outside, me and Od'z made our way to the bus stop. Moments later Smithy bopped out the arcade with the older boys. He looked proud of himself. As though he had won. I was confused by his reaction. He didn't win no fight. So why was he coming out looking so boasy? I didn't even watch that coz I knew I would see him at school the following week. I was going to break his face in a fair one-on-one. Od 'z told me that I had a lump just above my eye. It made me even more vex. This was the first time anyone had ever bruised my face. It affected my ego big time. For that reason I was going to make an example of Smithy. Rah! Three fights in one day. Yesterday none of these guys were enemies. Now I feel like if I don't come back hard, my rep's at stake.

When I got home that evening my brother saw the lump on my face and asked me what happened. When I told him, he switched and asked who did it. "I don't know bruv, but they were definitely older Tottenham boys for a fact."

"Okay, say nuffin. I'm coming on Monday."

Monday morning, I made my way to school and met up with my bredrins. When we got there we went straight to registration. As soon as I stepped in the classroom I got sent straight back out. I was told that the Head of year wanted to see me. When I saw the Head she told me to go home coz I was permanently expelled from school. They knew about the fight. Furthermore who had told them? They didn't even want to hear my side of the story. I was so angry and frustrated I could have cried.

The decision to expel me was unfair; there were two people involved and only one was punished. The school didn't care. My brother was home when I got there. I told him I had just been expelled. He had already planned to come to the school that day and he wasn't going to change his mind. I was going along with him to handle my business. Geezer's older brother, Natty, was also at my house and decided to roll with us.

We left my house in good time so we could get to D&K just before 3.30. I rolled with a metal pole tucked in my sleeve, ready to do damage. Mr Modi, the deputy head, was standing at the school gate when we got there. He asked us to leave. I didn't pay him no mind. I had no reason to care about school rules no more. I had been kicked out with no explanation. No one wanted to hear my side of the story. I didn't see why I should now listen to him or anyone else.

We pushed past him. My brother was about to attack him but saw he was scared so he left him. Modi ran back into the school. Probably to call the police. A huge crowd followed us. It was a madness. Along the way I grabbed some older boys in Smithy's year. "Where's Smithy? Where is he?" I shouted.

The boys I stepped to were bigger than me and, to my surprise, shook up when I grabbed them. It kinda felt good, I felt powerful. Having beef put us in the limelight; it was like being on stage or on TV. Every one was watching us and we had to perform and make a serious statement. We searched around badding up the whole school looking for Smithy, but we couldn't find him. Someone told us he had run to the back entrance, so we made our way to the bus stop.
On our way we saw some well-known Tottenham boys around my brother's age standing by the school gate. One of them, Butcher, my brother knew. Usually the older Tottenham boys would be the so-called stars of the show at 3.30 but this afternoon was Hackney's time. And they didn't look too pleased about that. We still couldn't find Smithy, though. So we got a bus opposite the school to Wood Green headed for home. When we reached the next stop Butcher, and some other boys got on. My brother and Natty were sitting at the back of the bus. Me and Geezer were sitting about halfway down on opposite sides of the gangway.

The Tottenham boys bopped on the bus on some hype ting. "Tottenham man don't watch no face. Tottenham man don't watch no face," They started to put their hands on some of the younger boys' heads, telling them to get up coz they wanted to sit. They then headed towards the back of the bus. My brother and Geezer's brother Natty, jumped up. My brother said, "Nah, Butcher that's my people.".

I guess he didn't realise that the Tottenham boys were trying to steal back the hype that we had earlier. Both sides exchanged some screw face and then it kicked off.

Natty punched one them who went flying over some bus seats. My brother then gave his old bredrin Butcher a blow and he fell back. Butcher tried to kick my brother in the face but it didn't connect properly. I got my metal poll and then went to hit Lanky Steve who was the tallest. As I swung it back to lick him, Butcher's older bredrin grabbed it out of my hand from behind. He wanted to hit me but he held back coz he knew he was much older than me. I respected Taxman at that moment.

Boi-dem stormed on the bus in large numbers and the fighting stopped straight away. When we got off the bus my brother and Butcher got into a heated exchange of words. I joined in and started to run up my mouth and cussed after the Tottenham boys. We continued to argue and cuss with each other but the police presence stopped us from kicking off again. Me and my boys walked across the road and the Tottenham boys went their own way.

As we were making our way home, Geezer told us that he was going to Wood Green to hang out. This boy's ungrateful. This whole beef triggered off partly coz the Tottenham boys told him to get up out of the seat. And that's how he repays us! We warned Geezer that it wasn't the safe thing to do but he had other ideas. I suppose he felt bless coz he was going to meet some new Hackney gang called the Rowdy Bunch Boys.

Even his brother, Natty, was disappointed. Why's Geezer always on the beef when some stranger gives him a screw face, but when some well-known Tottenham boys tell him to get out of his seat he did nothing to defend himself? He didn't even make an attempt to have his own brother's back. From that day, I began to look at Geezer differently.

We got back to my house and, for some reason, my brother was still mad. I didn't understand why. "It was two of you against four of them," I said, "and you guys didn't lose. Everyone saw that, whether they were from Hackney or Tottenham."

He punched the wall nuff times, hard and fast. "I know Butcher. We grew up with him," he said.

I remembered how the three of us used to play an arcade game called Street Fighter in a kebab shop on Seven Sisters Road. And now we were street fighters. For real. I could see my brother was vex. It seemed like, since Popcorn's death everyone hated Hackney boys. Or they just wanted to get a name for themselves. Maybe they saw it as their chance to become a part of the beef that was brewing between Tottenham and Hackney. We didn't see ourselves as the enemy. But some of the people we had grown up with definitely saw us as Hackney.

A revenge attack was in place. That night many other Hackney boys turned up at our house to go and ride on some Tottenham boys. The house was filled with London Fields, Pembury and Holly Street boys. Even though I spent most of my childhood in Tottenham, from this moment onwards I felt I was forced to rep Hackney. My brother managed to get a van. The owner said he would drive them. I picked up my mum's rolling pin and I got ready to roll but my brother said, "Nah. This is for the big boys tonight."

I was pissed off. I wanted to have my brother's back to the end. And my ego wouldn't let me forget how Taxman had jacked my metal pole. I wanted another chance to make up for my performance on the bus earlier. Just as they were about to go, it started to snow. That didn't stop them though. They jumped in the van and went fishing for the Tottenham boys only to return a few hours later. I was relieved to see that they all got back safely. My brother told me that they had circled Tottenham and Wood Green but hadn't found anyone.

That night I went to bed and thought: rah this is mental! Friday to Monday, all of this beef, and it didn't even start from anything, other than that with Joel. My life is crazy. To top it off I don't even have a school to go to. And I have only just reached Year 9.

SELF-FULFILLING PROPHECY:
THE PROBLEM CHILD

My mum somehow managed to get a solicitor to appeal the decision to expel me from school. We went to a governors' meeting to get their final decision. When the solicitor had finished pleading my case, one of the governors said, "Nope, we don't want Robyn Travis back. We don't care what he has to say."

I spent the rest of that year at home bored out of my brains, having to hear the soundtrack to Richard and Judy in the mornings. I also had to do homework daily for my SAT exams. I hated being at home doing work which the school sent me. It just wasn't the same as being in a class with kids my own age. Mum made sure I was up to date with the school work. She also had me doing all types of house chores. It was like boot camp. I got fed up of being at home hearing nagging 24/7. We applied to schools near and far, but every single one refused to take me. I was officially labeled a problem and I believed it.

The older Holly Street boys who had already left school soon noticed that I wasn't going any more. To kill time I hung out with them around the manor. We went to bare schools in the area to draw gyal. We often got into beef and more time we ended up banging someone up.

My relatives weren't too pleased that I got expelled and was at home not getting a proper education. But there was nothing they could really do or say to change the situation. The only disappointment that affected me was my Nan's. She meant the world to me. I hated to disappoint her.

My brother was still dream chasing and still refused to let me become a part of his hustle. I still didn't see why not. My football dream was over. I missed the whole of Year 9 and I was only allowed back to sit my SATs, escorted through the school by the deputy head.

I didn't see the point and I more or less failed. I heard that Smithy and Joel's parents moved them to new schools. With all this time on my hands I started doing crazy stuff with the Holly Street boys to gain attention from the girls and respect from the mandem. Most boys our age were too scared to take the risks we did; like joyriding cars and peds or ordering takeaways on the phone and robbing the delivery man of the food. On the weekends, coming home from a dance, we would bump cabs or go up West to jack mobiles in Leicester Square or in Trocadero.

Sometimes I got into trouble and sometimes I didn't. Ending up in a police cell or in court was routine. I gave up caring whether I ended up in Feltham. But I could see I was putting my mum under a lot of stress. Whenever the courts found me not guilty, I could see the relief from my mum's body language and the look on her face.

I was a problem child who wanted to be in school like a normal child, so I could follow my fading dreams of becoming a famous footballer. I made up my mind to try hard to stay out of trouble. But the upcoming summer would be a testing time for me.

DEFEND THY BREDRIN

The summer holiday of '99 was about to begin and part of my life would be a bit more normal coz my school friends would be with me. I went to D&K to meet up with my bredrins on the last day of term. I waited at the school gate for Geezer, Od'z and some others. When they came out we caught the bus to Wood Green and chilled for a bit before heading home. On the way Geezer got a phone call. A boy called Gravy wanted a re-match rock with him. Me and Od'z followed him to Pellerin Road in Stokey to have his back. Geezer was my boy so I didn't care who this person was or why he wanted to fight. I had love for all my mandem and I was going to defend them to the end. Even if they didn't always have the same mentality.

When we arrived the Rowdy Bunch Boys, who Geezer rated, were standing there. They walked with us to an estate just off Pellerin Road. Gravy was waiting for him on the patch of grass in the middle of the estate and immediately they rocked it out.

I stood watching, thinking how shit this fight was. Geezer was definitely having a bad day. Frustrated, I switched and gave Gravy a stiff right uppercut. His eyes began to roll back and he was out cold. The Rowdy Bunch Boys were laughing. "Oh my god, Robyn knocked him out cold," I heard one say.

Me, Geezer and Od'z didn't hang around. We kept it moving and bopped home. Back in the endz, Geezer was screwing. "What's wrong, blud?" I said. "What you so vex for?"

"You stole man's stripes, blud," he said.

So that's what it's about. He didn't see it as me having his back and saving him from the embarrassment of defeat. He felt it took his street ratings. Worse still, he felt that I defended him to impress his Rowdy Bunch 'heroes'. I wanted to slap him. This was the second time that I realized that me and Geezer were not the same. He was ungrateful. I wish I'd paid more attention the first time but I vowed that from now on, I would never ever have his back in a one-on-one fight again. No matter what happens. I would let him fight on his own. Even if he was being battered. It would be hard for me to keep this promise coz I had love for Geezer and I saw my bredrins as my brothers.

Although there was a Hackney v Tottenham war going on, it didn't stop me and Geezer from going to Tiverton to chill with Od'z and our other Tottenham bredrins. Apart from the one incident on the bus I wasn't involved in the Tottenham v Hackney beef coz I still had friends in Totty.

It was the older Tottenham boys who seemed to hate us Hackney boys. My brother didn't like the idea of me going to Totty coz he didn't trust most of them. Neither did I, so I understood his concern but I didn't like limiting myself to which areas I went to.

E8 vs E8 - HATE WITHOUT A CAUSE

Weeks after the fight with Gravy, me, Geezer and some others were chilling in Holly Street late one evening when our older bredrin Risky-Talent said he heard there was a big fight happening down the road in London Fields Estate between one of the older Rowdy Bunch Boys and an older Fields boy. We were so bored that we decided to take the short walk to Fields to watch the older Hackney mandem fight.

There was no fight when we got there so the eight of us decided to chill on the estate. We were having our usual cussing matches when Geezer decided he wanted to go to the shop. He had barely gone when, out of nowhere, a group of boys turned up. There were about seventeen of them between 14/16 years old. I knew most of them from London Fields Primary. And there were others in the group I used to hang with in the Fields area when I first moved to Holly Street. We looked at each other and said, "Wah gwarn." Then Risky-Talent began to stir things up by dissin the Fields boys in a jokey manner. "You Fields boys ain't ready for my Holly Street boys".

Some of them laughed and others took the bait. "Nah, not me bruv, not me," one of them replied. Risky-Talent continued to wind them up. "None of you can beat Robyn in a one-on-one. No way." Some of them smiled but didn't agree. I heard some of them say, "Robyn's a rocker, though." I nearly took the bait myself. Luckily I remembered that these boys were once my friends. I wasn't going to let anyone stir up beef between us over no foolishness. Risky-Talent continued to run jokes. We all laughed, ignoring his comments. Then me and

Wildcat, who I knew from Fields, decided that we should all have a big play fight. Holly Street vs Fields. It sounded like fun, but only me, Risky-Talent and Geezer were from Holly Street. Geezer returned from the shop looking confused to see all the Fields boys. He looked even more confused to hear me and Wildcat talking about having a fight.

Risky-Talent saw that Geezer was on the beef and began to jokingly stir it up again. The Fields' boys laughed. Geezer was short with a short temper, but they didn't know him the way I knew him. "Relax, bruv. It's only a play fight." Geezer was too heated to listen. He heard me loud and clear but his ego covered him like earmuffs.

Risky-Talent's laughing was definitely having an effect on all our egos. He was very skilled at running jokes and winding people up. That was just his thing. By this time Geezer had had enough. He turned to my old friend Mannix and Paper Boy and shouted, "suck yuh mudda." Then they said it back to him. They both wanted to fight him and he wanted to fight them. I tried to remind everyone that this was supposed to be a play fight, but by now it was too late. Paper Boy and Geezer were ready to fight so Risky-Talent became the referee. I was vex that it had turn serious, but they were both on the beef. There was nothing left to say. Paper Boy removed his earpiece then it was on.

I reminded myself that I weren't gonna get involved in Geezer's one-on-one fights. But if my past friends had attempted to jump Geezer I would've lost my temper and turned on them. It wasn't in my heart to turn against the Fields boys. But I wouldn't have been able to stand there and watch Geezer get hurt. Especially if he was losing badly.

The scrap didn't last long. Risky-Talent broke it up after one vicious minute of fighting. To my relief no one else got involved. By now it was dark and I didn't see every punch connect but from what I saw they both took some licks. I know who I believe won, but it was a close scruff. I respected both of them. Geezer walked away looking vex. For some reason I felt bad for him so I followed. We had only gone a short distance when the Fields boys started shouting, "Come out the manor! Come out the manor!"

I wasn't sure if they were talking to me or Geezer so I didn't take it on. A few minutes later we were back in Holly Street catching up with some of the other boys in the area, talking about what had just happened down the road in Fields. Although we had walked away, some of us decided that we should go back up there. There was so much talk about what had just happened that we'd convinced ourselves that we had let Geezer down. So me, Marcus, Reckless, JJ, Darker and nuff others made our way back to Fields on behalf of Geezer but without him. On our way there some of the boys must have had a change of heart, coz the closer we got the smaller and smaller the team got. Certain man just weren't on it.

When we arrived at the Fields side of Middleton Road E8, it was about ten o'clock. The Fields boys were still there but in larger numbers. There was about thirty of them ranging from 14/16 year olds, with a couple of their olders who were about nineteen. In our group there was about ten of us between the ages of 14/15. Plus Risky-Talent and JJ, who were about eighteen. I was fourteen at the time. Some of the Fields boys were my old friends like Kane who I was tight with at London Fields Primary. But these times were different. It didn't really matter to us that we were outnumbered. I think our confidence was high coz we knew we were from an area which had a very bad rep before the tower blocks and flats got knocked down. I guess we were trying to live up to that rep. I also knew that there were some good rockers from Holly Street who I believed weren't afraid to get it on.

After a couple minutes two of the older Fields boys tried to diss the programme. "Holly Street ain't saying nothing since they knocked down the tower blocks and the old flats." All of us youngers were offended. Deep down I knew he was right. We simply didn't have the numbers that we had before the demolition.

My boy Marcus stepped up to defend the endz. "Who wants to fight me, one-on-one?" No one replied. They must have been intimidated by his size coz he was about six feet tall and only fifteen years old. Wilddcat was either one of the leaders of the Fields boys or just the cocky one. He smiled at Marcus. "Ok, we'll see when Large-P comes" he said.

After a few seconds, this boy who was about six feet five inches tall came running through London Fields Park. Marcus stood ready. Marcus and Large-P leapt at each other and grabbed one another in mid-air before crashing to the ground with a massive thump.

The Fields boys seemed to gain confidence and went to rush Marcus. I made my move. I was the first of the Holly Street boys to get involved. I ran over and sparked my old friend Wildcat in the face. Then I got jumped by some other Fields boys. Even though I was getting jumped I could still see who was backing the beef. I only saw Od'z and Risky-Talent backing it. Risky-Talent jumped in and helped Marcus.

Why ain't the rest of da mandem backing it? What a joke. JJ and others did nothing - they were spectators. While I was getting rushed my mobile phone rang. "Oi! Wait! Wait!" I shouted. Believe it or not, everyone stopped fighting. I answered my phone. It was my mum. I told her that I was down the road sorting something out and would be home soon. When I hung up everyone backed off and went their separate ways. No one ran.

We didn't know it at the time, but this was officially the first day of the so-called 'postcode wars' between Holly Street E8 and London Fields E8. We ran jokes about the boys who disappeared before we got to Fields, and those who came but didn't back the beef . I wasn't angry about the boys who didn't back it. They had all sorts of excuses. I believe they were just scared. I couldn't understand why they couldn't just keep it real and say they were shook.

I left da mandem and went home. I looked at a class picture of me when I was in London Field's Primary. I couldn't believe that I had just gone to war with most of my old classmates. Even though it started over foolishness, I decided I was going to back the area where I lived from now on - Holly Street E8.

In bed later that night I began to think about the madness. I was proud of Marcus and the way he handled himself. A year earlier I had told him not to be scared of Risky-Talent who had bullied him ever since they had a fight and Risky-Talent's shirt got ripped. It wasn't nobody's fault, but Risky-Talent made it clear that Marcus had to pay for it. He made Marcus pay hundreds for a shirt that probably cost fifty boof. That's how it goes. In the endz you've got to stand up for yourself or man will take liberties and make your life hell. But the way Marcus performed against the Fields boys in the beef gave him the respect he needed. This status now made him one of the main boys in our crew. I was really happy for him.

The summer of '99 was now over. I was approaching year 10 and I still didn't have a school to go to. I was due to have an interview with Daniel House, a pupil referral unit in Stokey. When I arrived there I was shown round the classroom. I saw Gravy, the boy I knocked out for Geezer earlier that summer. I also saw Wildcat from Fields who I sparked in the beef between Holly Street and Fields. The teacher told me I would be in the same class as them. I turned to her. "Look miss, I'm really not that bad, y'know. I really wanna go back to a normal school and focus on my football. If you let me go back to school I promise I'll be on my bestest behaviour. No fights, no bunking, I'll even wear loafers, if I have to."

Everyone laughed. "We'll see how you get on here first," she said. A few weeks later I was accepted at Kingsland which was only a ten minute walk from Holly Street. I didn't show it, but I was really happy to be back at normal school especially after I was rejected everywhere else. I settled in easily and the rest of the year went quickly. I was disappointed that the school didn't have a football team. It didn't surprise me doh coz this was Hackney and I've never known Hackney to invest in their youth.

I started late in year 10 and would have wanted to do GCSE drama and P.E. but since I wasn't given a choice I became less motivated and was no longer excited about being back in a school. I kept to my word, doh, and stayed out of trouble. I even wore loafers. Those shoes made my Holly Street boys run joke on me: The Fresh Prince of Kingsland! During school hours I hung around mostly with girls to avoid confrontation, but as soon as 3:30 came around I was back to being Robyn Travis, the Holly Street bwoy.

ADDING FUEL TO THE FIRE

So far '99 had been a crazy year for me. Old friends from Fields were enemies. I no longer felt safe going to Tottenham. My dreams of becoming a famous footballer were fading. And, I still had money problems. My brother still didn't want me chasing dreams, so jacking mobile phones without him knowing became my only way of surviving.

Mum talked about marrying her old boyfriend, Smoking-Joe. She asked me and my brother how we would feel if she got hitched. We weren't feeling it at all. We didn't want another man in the house. Junior wasn't a good experience for her or us. But we agreed for her happiness.

My first impression of Smoking-Joe was that he was cool, and as long as he didn't disrespect my mum or try to play daddy, everything would be fine. He moved in soon after they got married. After a few months he started to change and did some really strange things. One day I came in to find him lying naked on the dining room floor. He wasn't moving and I couldn't hear him breathing. I thought he was dead. Then he coughed. I was so angry and disgusted with what I saw, I went straight to bed.

Sometimes I would be in my room chilling and my brother would kick down the door and grab me up, accusing me of stealing his dreams. We used to argue and fight about it. He would always win, doh, I just couldn't beat him. I used to be mad coz he didn't believe I hadn't touched his dreams. I was even madder that I took a beating for something I didn't do. When he tried it again, I switched and picked up a borer to stab him but mum broke it up.
A few days after, one of our cousins told my brother that he had

seen Smoking-Joe outside a crack house. Mum's new husband was a crack head? That's when we realised who was stealing my brother's dreams. Me and my brother made up. It was now time to break the bad news to mum, but she didn't seem to take it seriously. She always tried to see the best in people. But her husband couldn't control his habits. We also found out that he was an alcoholic and he wasn't working.

When a crack head is trying to support their habit, they will do whatever it takes to get the money for the next fix. On one occasion, me and my friends came back to my house after a shubz. Everyone decided to stay over, so we went to sleep in the front room. When we woke up the next morning my phone was missing. I didn't blame any of my bredrins coz my suspicions told me that this was crack head behaviour. Tension and issues of trust grew and became a huge problem in our house. Mum always defended her husband against me and my brother. Sometimes when me and mum argued, she would lose her temper and punch me in the face for being disrespectful.

I soon fell out with her husband. Enough was enough. His behaviour was embarrassing me on road. His addictions were becoming evident to people on the estate and the embarrassment was too much to deal with. I was mad coz my mum wasn't taking any action. So I told her if I saw him high in the house or on the doorstep again I would deal with him. "You're my son, you don't run my life. And if you touch him it will be me and you inside here," she said. After that disagreement we never really saw eye to eye again.

A few weeks later I was coming home from school with a few of my Holly Street boys after chilling at Mcdonald's in Dalston. When I got close to my house I saw my mum's husband lying on the ground by the front door. He was clearly stoned out of his head. He looked up and just ignored me. I stepped over his body, kicked him and told him to move from the door. He carried on ignoring me. The humiliation of my friends watching added more fuel to the fire. I switched, went to my room, got my baseball bat, went back out and started to hit him.
He got up and stumbled in the middle of the road. I continued to beat him with the bat coz I wanted him clear out of my sight. Out of

nowhere, I felt some hard punches to my face. As I turned to swing my bat I saw it was my mum. I dropped the bat. I was so hurt. It felt as though she turned against me for a crack head and alcoholic. I started to lose love and respect for her soon after.

It was a hot weekend in May 2000. I was woken up by Reckless in my room, shaking me and shouting. "Robyn, wake up. The Fields boys that rushed you and Marcus are kicking ball in Queensbridge". I was half-asleep and drowsy from hayfever tablets, but slipped on my trainers and bopped across the road with Reckless to the Leisure Centre. We walked into the hall and saw up to thirty Fields boys on the pitch.

My ego couldn't handle them coming to Holly Street to play football peacefully. No way could I let them do that, coz when we went to Fields they rushed us. Holly Street's bad boy image had to be defended. I was ready to rep my endz. I recognised nuff of them from the fight a year ago. Like me, most of them were 14 years old, and a few of them were a bit older. The main boy leading the group was three years older than me. I walked on to the field in the middle of their game and shouted, "Every one of you who rushed me in Fields that day, come outside and fight me, one-on-one. Now!"

I turned around but fear had got the better of Reckless. He was gone. I was on my own surrounded by Fields boys. Devon, who was eighteen, started running his gum that me and him should have a one-on-one. He must have mistaken me for someone who backs down. "Whoever wants it can have it," I shouted. We began to walk towards each other, but just before it kicked off my brother, Risky-Talent, Clint and Marcus came bursting in. Thank you God, you sent back-up just in time.

I made my way out to await my chosen opponent, Devon went on his phone to call some more Fields boys to come and back the beef. Even though there were only five of us from Holly Street and there was, like, six times as many of them. At least.

Who cares, doh. Holly Street's my town. There's no way anyone's gonna rush me outside my house. I'm not havin' it. Word must have got out coz people gathered to see what was going on. Olders from

Fields turned up; some of them were in my living room just the previous year, ready to roll with my brother when the Tottenham beef kicked off .

One of the tallest boys was chosen to fight me. It had to be my old friend Kane. As it was me who started it this time, as we squared up towards each other I couldn't stop thinking about how stupid this beef was getting. I smacked him in the face. We exchanged punches, blow for blow. At one point the fight was broken up as the police drove past. Then it was on again. It was an equal fight at first, but when I landed my last few shots I knew I was winning. I could hear my brother and Risky-Talent screaming, "Knock him out. Finish him." Blood was everywhere so I left it. I knew I had won and so did everybody else. I had nothing more to prove. The fight was over, me and my brother walked home.

I went indoors to chill and put some ice on my lip. There was non-stop knocking at my front door from people in the area, all bigging me up saying, "Nuff respect bwoy, you repped Holly Street." My so called friend Reckless then showed up. He sat next to me and started to big me up. "Ah you dat, Rob!"

"So where did you disappear, Houdini?" I asked.

I couldn't understand why such a big muscular guy like him would vanish as soon as the beef started. Plus, he was a couple of years older. In my eyes he was a waste of hench. I knew I couldn't depend on him to have my back if beef kicked off.

WATER'S THICKER THAN BLOOD

At the beginning of the Summer of 2000, Holly Street boys were mixing a bit more with the Rowdy Bunch Boys. This was mainly coz Risky-Talent, Reckless and Geezer were associated with them and would bring them around Holly Street to hang out. They had recently started to have beef with the Pembury boys. On one occasion, the Rowdy Bunch Boys were jammin with some of my Holly Street boys in Dalston MacDees. Me and Marcus decided to go to link up with the rest of da mandem but before were got to leave Holly Street we saw them approaching and they seemed to be on some hype ting.

"Oi, you man, believe, we just had a madness with dem older Pembury boys," one of them said. We were all talking about the incident when someone got a phone call. I could hear screaming down the phone. The person was saying, "There's nuff Pembury boys and Fields boys on Queensbridge Road and they are about to rush Geezer." Part 2 of the beef had kicked off. Round the corner. We sprinted to Queensbridge to see over forty Fields boys and Pembury boys surrounding Geezer.

Me, Wade, Darker, Marcus and, surprisingly Reckless, charged at them and a few blows were exchanged. Even though there were only fifteen of us, the forty odd boys backed off for some reason and started bopping towards Fields.

Apparently Reckless had shouted, "Go and get your leader Damage." We picked up Geezer and asked him if he was OK. We walked him to his house and that's when we realised that he had been stabbed in the upper leg. It wasn't life threatening, at least not immediately. The Fields boys also had the cheek to take his bike. We couldn't let them get away with sutt'n like that, so man had to go and get revenge for Geezer.

Within an hour or so I found out that it was my old classmate Artful Dodger who had taken the bike. But we never found out who used the knife. At this point I was mad that they had taken our little beef to a different level by using weapons. This was officially developing into a very nasty war.

I was ready to roll out but the Rowdy Bunch boys started leaving. They said they was gonna go and get some more mandem. I thought it was strange, especially since the Pembury boys were more their enemies than ours. If they didn't come back, we weren't gonna have the numbers to go to war. We left Geezer's house and got tooled up. We gathered outside to make sure everyone was ready to roll. There weren't many of us. It was me, Darker, Mintz, Wade, Reckless, Marcus, Risky-Talent, and a few others. Some of the other Holly Street boys knew what had happened to Geezer but they never came to have his back. Holly Street was a dodgy area. It seemed that certain peeps conveniently avoided being present to back it when any real beef kicked off.

As we were waiting for more recruits the boi-dem drove by slowly in a convoy of bully vans. We all dashed our weapons in the bushes, just in time. Soon after, my brother passed by with two older Holly Street boys. My brother agreed to roll with us, but he had to go home. Everyone was getting hyped coz we heard that the Rowdy Bunch and other mandem from the area were on their way. Many of my boys were boasting about what they were gonna do.

I was too angry for all that hype talk. I stayed silent and focused. Wade left the group for a moment then came breezing right back from round the corner shouting, "There's nuff of dem. They're coming, they're coming." They must have been chasing him coz in a matter of seconds one car pulled up, then another and another. Groups of boys carrying knives and baseball bats walked quickly alongside the cars. None of my Holly Street boys had weapons coz we hadn't had a chance to get them from the bushes.

Risky-Talent ran up to the first car and said, "Wah gwarn." I was in shock to see he was trying to be friendly with the enemy. He knew it wasn't time for no chit-chat, Chups! Maybe he was just trying to save his skin. I casually walked up to the large crowd of Fields boys who were marching towards us. I attacked the first person I came into contact with, which happened to be my old friend Mannix. He swung a baseball bat at me and I threw a punch at the same time. The bat caught me on my neck. My punch connected with his face. He swung at me again. This time the bat hit my arm. I trapped the bat with the same arm whilst punching him in the face. Some of his crew came to help him out so I started throwing punches at everyone. I was on top form and felt that nobody could stop me.

Then all of a sudden I felt a solid blow to my stomach and fell to one knee. Rahtid! That was a good punch. I got back up and was just about to start fighting again when I heard Geezer's mum and stepdad shouting from their drive way, "Run, Robyn, run." No. No way. I ain't running from nuffin. I looked back to see all my so-called friends scatter like mice. When the fight first started I had this feeling that I was swinging it out on my own. It hurt me when I saw my boys running off, but I felt I had to stay and fight. I couldn't forget that these same Fields boys had rushed and stabbed Geezer earlier that day. "Robyn, run; you've been stabbed."

I froze, looked down at my stomach and realised it was a low blow. Stabbed. Me? I staggered towards my yard. The pain started to sink in, I pulled up my t-shirt and saw blood running like tap water - the hole in my stomach was massive. God, I can't die now. My mum'll kill me.

I went to my neighbour's; they were like family anyway. I knocked and patiently waited for an answer. Cherrie opened the door and I limped inside the dining room where a couple of people were cotching. "I just got stabbed," I said calmly. I tried my best not to cause a scene but when they saw the amount of blood pouring from the hole in my t-shirt, everyone panicked. Someone called the ambulance while Gloria put a tea towel on my stomach. She pressed it on the wound. I was losing nuff blood. Someone must have called my mum and brother coz they soon turned up, looking shocked but calm. I was finding it hard to breath. I thought I was gonna die.

My brother got fed up of waiting and said, "Forget the ambulance. I'm taking him in my car." In the car journey I kept falling asleep but whenever we went over the speed humps, I felt a sharp pain in my stomach which would wake me. All I could hear was my brother and mum shouting, "Robyn, stay awake, don't close your eyes. We're nearly there."

At Homerton Hospital they helped me to A&E. My clothes were soaked in blood. One of the receptionists at the desk looked at me and asked, "Do you know what you got stabbed with?"

How the hell would I know? Why does it matter? Maybe I should phone the boy who stabbed me and ask him. "Naaaah, sorry, I don't." I smiled.

Next thing I remember is being on a bed with tubes in my arms. My mum was standing on my right and Geezer's mum was standing on my left. There were also a few doctors working to save my life. I tried to talk, to tell mum not to worry, whatever happens I'll be okay, but I couldn't open my mouth. I heard a boy in the next bed making noise. I heard Geezer's mum say it was her eldest son, Natty, who had been stabbed in the leg. I don't think that his stabbing was as serious as mine, coz his mum spent most of the time by my bedside. Seeing his mum there had me shitting myself without showing it. It's like everyone thought I was going to die.

BATTLE OF THE MIND

"Young man, you're very, very lucky," one of them said. "You could have died here tonight." Died. I was awake until the early hours, replaying the whole thing in my head over and over again. I was in a lot of pain. Physically and emotionally. Did my friends really leave me to war all alone? Who the hell stabbed me? Rahtid, did my man say I nearly died?

I had a hundred and one thoughts and questions in my mind. Reality was kicking in and my whole world was turning upside down. I argued with myself about revenge. It felt like there were two different Robyns in one body. One, with the dreams and aspirations of escaping the inner city ghetto. The other, whose heart was turning as cold as ice with demons telling him he had to kill everyone from Fields.

The second Robyn was winning. From that day on, it didn't matter whether we grew up as friends or not, they brought knives into this beef. Now it's time to get wicked. The pain from the stab wound affected me so much I couldn't sleep. I wanted to kill whoever stabbed me so badly, but I didn't even know who it was. It didn't even matter who done it. Kill them all, fam. They were all the same.

But, the more reasonable side of me replied, "I hear you, bruv. It come like they've forgotten who man are. Like man's some prick. It don't make sense getting twenty-five years for lickin' down the wrong man, though. 'Llow that. You have to find out exactly who done it. That's the righteous thing."

I had this strange argument with myself for hours. The two sides of me finally agreed on one thing though: it was time to discharge myself. The doctors were furious at my decision to leave. "What are you doing? You were stabbed near your kidney. We still have to do tests to see if any damage has been done."

"If it gets worse I'll come back," I rolled out of bed in agony, barely able to walk. My stomach had been patched up but I had lost a lot of blood. My murderous rage refused to be defeated. My pride refused to lie in a bed like a victim. They gave me some painkillers and other tablets, plus a pair of crutches. They still tried to convince me to stay but after my near-death experience I just wanted to go home.

The minicab arrived. It was a hot Saturday morning on the streets of Hackney and everybody was going about their business. As we approached Richmond Road, a short distance from Holly Street, I noticed how close the Fields boys and Holly Street boys blocks were. No more than 800 metres apart.

Back home I tried to relax but my internal revenge battle started again. I wanted blood. I wanted it so badly. I had to think this through. The different voices in my head were in conflict.

VOICE OF THE STREETS: Let me get this straight. First they rush you, and now they're stabbing you. Chups! Dem man have taken it to a next level. Come on, Rob, they stabbed you like you're some stranger to dem. That's just fuckeries."

VOICE OF REASON: I hear you, it come like no one fights fair any more and fists ain't the only weapons. But once you kill someone there's no going back.

VOICE OF THE STREETS: Bruv, this righteous ting ain't working for you. It's gonna get you killed. Even in the Bible it says an 'eye for an eye and a tooth for a tooth.'

Eventually reason lost out to revenge. I decided it would be fair to kill. Under certain conditions:

1. Not to kill anyone until I found out exactly who stabbed me so that

justice could be served.

2. Not to carry out vengeance til things cooled down. Right now, everybody would know I had a motive.

3. To do it alone. I couldn't trust anybody not to snitch if we got caught. Nor could I depend on them to be mentally ready to take it as far as I wanted to.

4. Not to tell anyone what I was planning.

5. Not to let it turn me into a prisoner to the streets. After I kill who stabbed me, I'll carry on with my life as normal and set new goals to eventually get out of the ghetto of Hackney and never come back.

6. Most importantly - don't get caught.

I stayed in my bedroom for most of the afternoon. Still in pain. The painkillers couldn't deal with the hurt I was feeling about my friends leaving me for dead and not coming to see me in hospital. Maybe it was the shame of them not having my back that kept them away. Maybe they thought I had died or sutt'n and couldn't face it. If any of my bredrins got stabbed I would have been the first person at the hospital. Whatever the outcome. I wouldn't have been able to sleep without knowing they were going to be okay. I pushed those thoughts to the back of my mind, trying to convince myself that it wasn't that big of a deal. I didn't want to stay in the house all day like some victim. I needed to show everyone that I wasn't affected by what happened. I picked myself up, took my crutches and went out on the estate to show face. I had to prove that I couldn't be broken and that fear doesn't live in the heart of Robyn Travis. Not any more. And if any fear remained in him, he was going to kill it.

I opened the front door to see Marcus standing there, his head down in disgrace. "You cool, bruv?" he said.

I nodded and followed him across the road to his yard. The minute we got there his mum said, "I heard you got stabbed last night, Robyn. You okay? It's a good ting Marcus wasn't there."

I looked at Marcus waiting for him to tell his mum that he was there but I guess he didn't want her to know that he was involved in the street life. We left his mum's and stopped near my yard and chilled for a bit. "How you gonna leave man like that. How could you run and leave man for dead?"

"Bruv, I'm really sorry I ran off and left you. I froze. My bad. It will never happen again. You're my boy and I should've had your back. Whenever you're ready to roll on dem Fields boys lemme know. I'm ready."

Marcus' readiness to roll had little affect on me. I had lost all faith in him. How could I ever trust him to back me 100% when beef got real sticky? I had love for my boy all the same. I picked up the crutches and bopped home in pain. Physically and emotionally. I hadn't got far when Marcus called out. "Robyn, Robyn, Fields boys."

I hopped as fast as I could across the road. I couldn't wait to buss some Fields boy's head with my crutches. It turned out to be some Fields olders, Damage and Matlock. They pulled up beside me and rolled down the window. Damage said, "Robyn, why you backing these fake Holly Street boys for? They're not like you. Anyway, you're originally a Fields boy. Look how long you know my likkle brother Mannix. You two were friends from long time."

He looked at me as though he was disappointed. "Me and your brother are cool," he said. "We didn't come for you last night. We came down for this fool next to you and that loud mout' Reckless. Whoever stabbed you took it too far, and when you and your bro' decide to retaliate, I'm not getting involved."

I respected Damage's words and felt like a bit of an idiot for getting caught up in such a silly beef. He was right. I was friends with his brother way before I even knew most of the Holly Street boys.

Damage and Matlock drove off but not before calling Marcus a pussy' ole. I leaned on my crutches and struggled home. When I got there I went to my room and tried to get some much needed sleep. But people wouldn't stop knocking the front door. Friends and family. For once I didn't want no one around me. I was going through madness and wasn't sure who my real friends were. I didn't want any fake people in my personal space. Later that night my older cousin Bread came to my house. He hadn't heard about what happened.

"Why you posing with those crutches for?" he said. "You looking sympathy, you little attention seeker."

I laughed. "Nah, I got stabbed last night."

He switched. "What? Who bored up my likkle cousin? These kids must be fucking crazy. Get in the car now and show me who done it."

We got in his car and went to Fields. There was a group of about fifteen boys hanging around when we got there. I was still in mad pain and for the first time ever I was wearing a cap to disguise my appearance. We jumped out the car just outside Grand Union and I turned my cap backwards. That's when the Fields boys recognised me. They seemed shocked to see me back in their manor less than 24 hours after I was stabbed.

Without waiting, my cousin marched up to them. I left my crutches in the car and followed as best I could. "Are these the boys, yeah?" my cousin asked. I could see in his eyes that he was ready to kill any one of them. From the looks in their eyes, each one of them Fields boys could see he meant business. Some of them were actually involved in our war the night before. But this wasn't the time. I wanted to deal with them myself. I just wanted to show face today and send a clear message that it wasn't over. That I wasn't going to be broken by none of them. As far as I was concerned dem man cheated. Certain man didn't have the heart to go one-on-one with me, and I weren't no Bruce Leroy. I could smell the fear on them. I paused, thought about it, then turned to my cousin.

"Nah, cuz, it's not them. I don't know these yutes." The Fields boys were either too shocked or too shook to say anything. We got back in the car. My cousin revved the engine, pushed the gear into first and drove off. On the way home a strange feeling crept over me. Even though I had been stabbed, I felt more powerful than the Fields boys. Unlike them I didn't need a big crew round me to find the confidence to fight anyone at any given time. It was like a game of chess. All the players knew that the next move was mine. And when word got round that I had the nerve to come to their endz after all that had happened, they would all know that I wasn't scared of no one or nothing. I liked that feeling or maybe by that point I just didn't care any more. I really hoped the streets would start talking soon so that I could put a face to the hand that stabbed me, and my knife in the heart of that face.

PRISONER TO THE STREET

A few weeks later I was back in class. The year 11s had completed their GCSEs. There was no need for them to return to school. Just as well, coz amongst them were a couple of Fields boys. Only God knows what I would have done if I had bumped into them in the corridor or in the playground at break-time.

I was chilling outside my yard one day when I saw one of my so-called bredrins from the estate. "Rob, I know who stabbed you, y'know," he said. "It was your old bredrin Kane."

"Cool, cool. Dead man walking," I said.

I thought my mind would be at ease after hearing that news. But instead I became confused. Me and Kane had a fight a couple months earlier, but it was a fair one-on-one fight and it was possible that there would be a re-match. I had seen Kane nuff times since then and he never challenged me once. To sneakily stab me in my stomach was taking it too far. I didn't rate that. It was like some wolf pack mentality. For me there was no honor in it.

What really got me was the way it was done. I was scuffing three people on my own, and one of them had a baseball bat. I was already outnumbered. I couldn't believe how sneaky and cowardly Kane was to creep in and stab me on the sly. My soul felt empty. I went to sleep dreaming the same dream every night. Seeing Kane, running up to him and, without hesitation, stabbing him over and over again until I couldn't stab no more. Then getting rid of his body, burning my bloody clothes and going home to carry on as normal.

My values and morals were gone. I no longer cared about goals, dreams or my future. I gave up on forgiveness. All I could think of was murder. Without realising it I had become a prisoner to the streets.

Sometimes I woke up in cold sweats, unable to decide whether it was worth killing him or not. Most kids my age were probably thinking about girls, money or the lastest crep. I was thinking about duppyin someone and how to get away with it. I'd gone from dreaming about making it as a footballer to dreaming about murder. The streets were changing me. One morning I woke up from the same dream to see my mum standing in my room.

"Mum, you wouldn't believe who stabbed me, y'know."

"Who was it?" she asked.

"You remember my old friend Kane, the one you bought the crisps for when we first moved here." She stood there in shock. "Honestly mum, I can't live with myself unless I kill this guy. He deserves to die."

She started to preach to me about what God would do if I retaliated. "Son, leave it in the hands of God."

I kissed my teeth. "Nah, mum. God shouldn't have let it happen in the first place. If God sends me to hell for killing Kane, then God ain't just. Chups. But whatever..."

My mum was shocked at what I said but tried to understand my anger. I told her about the dreams I was having and that I would kill him without getting caught.

It wasn't a normal conversation between a mother and a son. The look in her eyes said it all. She was losing a son to the streets. She went silent as if to say, 'His mind's made up, I can't change it'. As hard as it was, I had to tell her just in case I did get caught. I didn't want her to find out from the police or even worse via the news. I imagined the headlines:

15-year-old Robyn Travis has been charged with the murder of 15-year-old Kane from Hackney who was stabbed eighty two times by his old friend.

I imagined if I got caught people would be quick too judge me harshly without knowing what led to my actions. I'd be labelled a murderer and seen as the bad bwoy who brought shame on my family. When he heard whodunnit, my brother went straight to Fields and staked out Kane's house, waiting for him to come home. I told him to 'llow it and let him live. I didn't want him to go to prison for me. I wanted to do this on my own and I was prepared to live with the consequences. I pleaded with my brother every day to forget about it. He wasn't too pleased but he eventually eased off.

As time went on I heard mixed messages from people on the Fields Estate. They told me that not every Fields boy was pleased that I got stabbed. One girl told me that Jadie and a few others who I was once friends with didn't agree with it. She confirmed that Kane was apparently remorseful. Another time I was chilling at my girl's house when she told me that one of the Fields boys was boasting about me getting stabbed. I was mad at first but when she told me who it was I just laughed. I didn't take it seriously. I had beaten him up previously. I'll deal with him when I see him.

It was now the summer holiday and I had recovered from the stabbing. I got a phone call from Aunty Jay, telling me that there might be a job for me if I was interested – she was trying to keep me off the streets. My Aunty's friend was one of the managers at a restaurant called Chiquitos in Leicester Square. I was given a day's trial at the restaurant and was later told that I got the job. It wasn't a job that I was proud of but I was happy that, at the age of fifteen, I was making money. I was a server's assistant: cleaning tables, drying cutlery, setting the tables and helping the waiters serve food. I was on minimum wage - £3.60 per hour. £310.00 after tax at the end of every month. I made more from tips. People would go out of their way to tip me. After two 10-hour weekend shifts I could leave with up to £40.00 in tips. I guess people liked me coz I was young and a hard worker. Growing up Mum was strict with house chores. She made sure that me and my brother did our fair share and that rubbed off.

Before I got stabbed I was always on the estate with my Holly Street boys coz I didn't have anything better to do. I was always thinking of ways to make money without selling drugs or robbing people's phones. With this job I finally had that chance. It felt strange, coz from Monday-Friday I was repping my endz and backing my boys to the fullest and willing to ride on enemies from rival areas. Then from Friday-Sunday I was cleaning tables in a restaurant and asking customers, "Can I take your order, please?".

I was living two totally different lifestyles and still had the scar on my stomach as a constant reminder of unfinished business. As the weeks went by, my life was mainly about work and school. At home there were still a lot of problems though. Smoking-Joe was always around, high on crack, and me and mum weren't exactly seeing eye to eye. Her love was blinding her and she didn't want no son of hers dictating her life. We were also about to get evicted and become homeless. Even the money I was earning from my job at the restaurant didn't make a difference.

One evening I came in from a long day's work. Mum called me and my bro into her room and said she wanted to talk to us. She looked like she had seen a ghost. "What's wrong, mum? What is it?"

"You guys are not gonna believe this," she said, sitting down, "but I just saw your dad."

I laughed nervously. "How mum, I thought you said he was dead?"

I wasn't the only one finding it hard to come to terms with what mum was saying. My brother was shocked. If looks could kill someone would have died.

"What did you say to him?"

"Nothing, son. I was so shocked I froze."

"Mum, how the fuck could you freeze? You said you just saw my dad, who's meant to have been dead all these years. Are you sure it was him?" I was wrong to be rude but I couldn't think straight.

"Yes, I'm sure," she replied. "I saw him on Graham Road near Mare Street."

I paused for a few moments. "So, mum, are you saying he faked his death or something?"

"Yes, son, that's what it looks like."

I was outraged and hurt. She had previously told me that my dad wanted her to abort me when he found out she was pregnant. Maybe he faked his death coz he didn't want me.

All those years I spent fighting anyone who said, "Your DAD." All that for a guy I didn't even know and who wasn't even dead. I didn't even know what the man looked like. I got so mad I felt sick. I went into my bedroom and started to smash up everything in sight. No one could calm me down. Soon afterwards I fell asleep on the floor.

I woke up the next morning haunted. Still very disturbed by my mum's revelation. I wasn't totally convinced that she saw my dad alive but then I know she definitely didn't see him dead. I didn't trust her judgment. And I didn't know my dad to judge. That's when I noticed my mum had left a photo of my Dad on the bed.

How could I trust anybody any more? My expectation of my Holly Street boys had changed when they left me to die. Our friendship was like one big lie. Everyone gave the big talk like they would ride or die for each other, but this wasn't the case. And if it's true that my dad left me and my brother with the pain of another big lie, then nuffink's real. No one's true. This bothered my brain for a long time to come.

The summer holiday of 2000 was now over. It was time to go back to Kingsland School to start Year 11 - my final year. I tried to ignore all the street talk about my stabbing. I wanted to wait until all the hype surrounding my name had died down. Then I'd move on Kane.

TARNISHED AND TAINTED

It was November; me, Darker and Marcus were chillin in Holly Street. Marcus had spotted Junior Demon, another boy from the estate who had apparently slept with his girlfriend. They got into a fight, Junior Demon was getting battered, and me and Darker had to break it up. When we got back to my house. Marcus started to sulk under the desk in my bedroom. Me and Darker was bussin' up coz it was funny to see a six foot boy under a desk, crying over some girl.

"I'm a dead man," Marcus bawled. "Junior Demon's big brother is a mad man. He'll come back for me."

"Don't watch that," I said. "We got your back. Ride or die. Just don't freeze like you did when I got stabbed." I went in to the cupboard where the garden tools were and gave him an axe, Darker a wrench and grabbed a hammer for my own insurance. We went outside to chill, waiting for the mad man to show up.

Minutes later we saw four grown men coming towards us. As they got closer, I told Marcus to stand firm and not show fear coz we could take them on. Before I knew it, Marcus was gone. He sprinted past the four big men. They breezed after him. I was shook about what they would do if they caught him, so I ran after them. Darker followed. We ran past Marcus's girl's house. She shouted from the window, "Marcus, why are you always running for? You're such a pussy."

I looked up. "Shut yuh noise, this is over you." Funny how fast fear can

Robyn Travis

make you run. By now Marcus had built up too much of a distance between him and the men. When they realised they weren't going to catch him they turned on me.

They grabbed me and marched me round the corner. One of them put a gun to my head and told me to phone Marcus and tell him to come back or he would kill me instead. So I did. I took out my mobile and called him. I couldn't believe it. Marcus started crying down the phone on some 'sorry' talk. I knew by his response that he weren't coming back.

"Do what you have to do," I told the gunman. By this stage it was more than just being loyal. I had no reason to care about life or death.

He pushed the strap against my head and told me to show him where Marcus lived.

We were standing right by Marcus's house and even though Marcus had left me for dead, I kept it real and acted like I didn't know. He continued to push the strap against my temple. The other men begged him to 'llow it but he wasn't taking no talk. I was afraid inside but I refused to show any fear. It didn't help matters. Junior Demon's brother didn't care for my attitude.

Just when I thought he was gonna pull the trigger, I heard a female voice call. "Robyn. Are you okay?" It was Marcus' sister. I felt the strap ease off. The gunman didn't stick around. He quickly left the scene. A crowd gathered, asking if I was okay. They knew something had happened but didn't know a gun was involved. I told them that I was bless. Junior Demon's mum also turned up looking for Marcus, who had the nerve to come strolling around the corner moments later. Junior Demon's mum didn't waste time. She ran up to him and whacked him in the head with a rolling pin. Most of the crowd seemed to think he deserved it. I didn't mention the gun. Not to Marcus' family nor mine. Truth is, I was more angry with Marcus for running and leaving me for dead. Again.

The friendship with my boys meant the world to me. There was nothing no one could say to separate me from them. But there were

84

signs which had me doubting whether the love and trust I had for them was mutual. Mum always said, "You think all these boys are your friends, huh? You'll soon find out."

A month after that madness with Marcus, we were evicted from our home in Holly Street and were officially homeless. I didn't want to live with my mum's crack head husband, so I was put into the care of social services. Me and my mum lost contact for at least two years after that. My brother was already eighteen at this stage so slept on the sofa at my Nan's one bedroom flat in an old people's building until he found long term accommodation.

Social services put me in Cape House. A B&B on Dalston Lane that used to be the police station. My room used to be a cell and had the same feel. The rules were very strict. You could only have two visitors at a time, and all visitors had to leave by 10pm. It was a shit place to live. Blatant addicts on either side of me. Most nights I couldn't sleep coz the fumes from their crack and heroin drifted under the door into my room. The shared kitchen and bathroom were beyond nasty. Sometimes I washed in the sink in my room other times I went to my Nan's. I tried my best to make the room feel like a home but I couldn't. It was uncleanable. Plus it had cockroaches and rats.

I wasn't used to living by the rule where I could only chill with two friends at a time. But since I got stabbed and left for dead, I still wasn't sure who my real friends were anyway. A couple of mandem, Darker and my girl buddies used to come and check for me. When I lived in a house, Geezer, Marcus and the rest of the crew always came round to chill. But I guess they were too good to come and cotch with a friend in a shit hole.

By this time I had become a qualified weed smoker. Whenever Mintz and Evil Kid came to check me in my room we would cover the smoke alarm with a plastic bag and get down to some serious blazing. The room was so small it got covered in a fog of weed in a matter of minutes. After visiting hours I would chill and blaze until morning with Tinchy and Sharon who lived downstairs.

I started blazing in Year 10 when I found out that Kingsland School didn't have a football team. It became my new hobby. School was becoming more than a joke. I never really went to lessons, I didn't see the point. I felt school had nothing to offer me and I didn't have nothing to offer school. But I did learn how to 'bill up' the perfect spliff. I spent most of my school hours blazing behind the sports block, getting lean with my friends.

I was so disconnected with school that sometimes I would do crazy things. On one occasion me and my friends bought a bottle of E&J brandy and stood in the playground to see who could drink the most. We got merry quick time, then went to our English lesson stinking of booze. It didn't seem to matter in this school. Most of the teachers couldn't care less. A few of them noticed me slipping academically and tried to get me to fix up and look sharp, but more time it seemed like they were having a go.

It was too late. By now my head was so far gone it didn't matter to me that I was no one at school. Where it mattered, was on the road side where I felt like I was somebody. Ms.Parry (head of year), Desta and Sandra (learning mentors), talked to me about everything that was going on in my life. Their intentions were good, but they had no idea where I was mentally.

In Year 11 everyone was getting ready to do their GCSEs about five months away. I knew I was failing so I decided, this school ting's not for me. I might as well do some extra shifts at work to make more cash. So that's what I did - I worked from 5 to 10 every day after school, then maybe do a midday to 10pm shift on a Saturday or Sunday. I would get home around 11 during the week, so tired that getting up for school would be a struggle. I wouldn't reach until after lunchtime and, before I knew it, it was time to go home or chill at MacDees in Dalston with my Holly Street boys.

We went there to look gyal and all da mandem would be there, Holly Street and Rowdy Bunch alike, running jokes and cussing matches was just standard. When Holly Street came together with Rowdy Bunch, it was bare jokes.

I didn't totally trust my Holly Street boys or the Rowdy Bunch since being stabbed, but it didn't stop me from linking up with them for jokes and cherps. When we were together it was like no one could chuck it to us. We were an army of youngers with a not-having it-from-no-one attitude. Hood stars. Commercial all over Hackney. We believed we ran tings in E8.

So you can imagine how I felt when I clocked Smithy, who got me expelled from D&K, passing by on the upper deck of a 76. We splurted after the bus to catch him and his friend dem to give them a couple licks, Holly Street style, but they jumped off and duss'd out before we reached.

That's how it was most days. Hype. Whatever was going down on the streets, when 4.30 came I would leave da mandem behind in Dalston and go to work cleaning tables.

Whenever I was on my J's I found myself thinking too much about my problems. I was coming to a realisation that I had nothing going for me and no one to really turn to. I was growing up way to quick and I felt like I was losing my true identity. The only way to escape my reality was by either billin' a spliff or cotching with da mandem on the block.

More time I cotched with da mandem coz it was the cheaper option. Holly Street boys had bare jokes /jokers. A day never passed when we weren't dissin' each other and it never took long for the dubbing match to start. Certain brudders took the joke too far. And what always started out as a joke ting sometimes ended up with certain man carrying certain feelings towards a next man.

Mix up or no mix up, I can't lie, I loved these cussing matches. Sometimes they were so funny, man would be dying of laughter. It didn't matter who had street ratings, when these matches started anyone could be top dog. It was always funnier when a member of the crew, lower in the ranks, was able to upset one of the top dogs. Holly Street is the funniest area of all the areas I ever lived in. It's why I liked to chill there so much, even though I wasn't feeling certain man in the team.

As well as me, Darker, Geezer and Pizza Boy seemed to be having it rough. Certain man around me had to get their grind on from young coz daddy wasn't around. I wasn't the only one. One or two of da mandem were even more desperate than me. I realised this the day Darker got a call from Pizza Boy asking us man to come link him outside Dalston MacDees.

"You lot get your food. I'm gonna come fly it in a minute."
We went in, got our food, and sat down without giving much thought to what he said. We were eating MacDees and running jokes when suddenly the doors flew open. As I turned I saw this mad yute with a big kitchen knife in his hand and a stocking over his head. As he walked pass us he nodded, as if to say, "Ah me dis." I realised it was Pizza Boy. He jumped over the counter and tripped. The cashiers screamed and ran to the back of the shop. He then started to tap the buttons on the tills but they wouldn't open. He threw some drinking straws on the floor in frustration and ran out. None of us had any idea that he was going to rob the place. I couldn't believe it. Pizza Boy actually had a pair of women's tights on his head. I had to laugh. That's gangsta. Now at least we knew what 'fly it' meant.

When we went back to Holly Street we found him moving low key on the estate, near Marcus' house. Marcus started to whinge. "Move from my house, bruv. MOVE! Why are you robbing MacDees, and coming outside my house for?" Me and Darker told Marcus to 'llow it. It was definitely a silly move. No doubt. My boy was slippin'. He couldn't have been thinking straight. But desperate times call for desperate measures.

THERE AIN'T NO JUSTICE - JUST US

My little job at the restaurant had me stacking some peas. Sometimes up to one-fifty a week on tips alone. Working dem ten-hour double shifts on the weekends was horrible. My back and legs would be killing me come midday. It felt like some modern day slavery business, without the licks of course. But who the hell was I to complain. Most boys my age didn't even have a job, and some were still living off mummy. I felt a sense of pride that people weren't seeing me as a hood rat, or some any-wotless-yute with no ambition.

Most of my colleagues at work were either white or latino. This was the first time in my life that I properly got to socialise with white people. In Hackney and Totty, the black population is high. Don't get it twisted or nothing, I saw nuff white people daily, but other than police, teachers and judges, the interaction between us and them was very rare. I guess we didn't have much in common. Certain white people would walk through Holly Street and wouldn't even answer when we politely asked for a cigarette or what the time was. Most of them would play deaf, ignore da mandem and keep walking with their head straight. So mixing with my white colleagues at lunch break had me feeling out of place. It took a while of spending time with them to feel at ease.

My little one nifty a week on tips wasn't really nothing to skank about. But it did do a great job of keeping me away from the streets. It even kept me away from acting out my plans of revenge. I didn't realise how much I needed a break from jammin on road and getting caught up in constant beef. Working and making an honest living felt like the righteous thing. A couple of da mandem who knew I worked hard to buy my 'ped' and chain would laugh and say, "You're not serious, Trav. Man like you should be out 'ere on the roads." I can't even lie, doh, the idea of giving up my job for the fast life was calling my name. But the idea of making a 'honest living' was calling me too. I felt bless enough to not stress it.

No matter what I did to earn legit paper, peeps still called me an undercover shotta and joked that I fitted the drug dealer description - whatever that means. Dem convos had me creasing up 'bout 'I've got a drug dealer face', yuh know. I dunno. Maybe it was the gold chain and new legit ped that had most man and certain gyal on road thinking dem way deh. Other than the chain I kept it low-key but that new exhaust from Japan was so loud you could hear me breezing before you even saw me eating road.

My moped was like the missus: I used to wifey that. More time, I was on some hype ting. Bussin' wheelies on all the bate high roads - Tottenham, Wood Green, Hackney, and even down Sout'. For once in my life I had money. I weren't bayding like a few drug dealers I knew. But every month's wages brought me closer to another Moschino shirt or Armani jeans. Or maybe even that £600 Avirex jacket like what my brother had. I could afford to buy some of the things that made me feel bless. I no longer had to squeeze my foot into crep that were too small, giving man bunions. Bun dem days of having to wear my brother's hand-me-downs. Fuck thinking of them younger days when I had to sew designer labels on my garms which mum bought from Ridley Market.

I found it strange that I didn't hear a lot of jokes from my friends about the type of work I did. Especially with the hype that surrounded my lifestyle. I had been asking the restaurant manager, Derek, about promotion for a while. Not just for the pay rise. I was fed up of being an assistant waiter. Cleaning tables all day everyday was driving me nuts. I was more than capable of taking on the greater responsibilities of being a waiter. But Derek never took me serious. Sometimes he would joke with another waiter in front of me. "What does the boy from Hackney need a promotion for?" I would buss a fake smile coz I didn't understand their sense of humour.

On one occasion I was in a 'not-havin'-it' mood for all these 'Hackney boy' jokes. So I confronted Derek. "I've been here for a year now on £3.60 an hour minimum wage and that's not enough. I don't get money from anywhere else. I have to look after myself. I need £4.75 an hour, just like all the others. How can other people come into the job after me and get promoted to waiter before me? What's that all about?"

Derek responded with the same 'Hackney joke', but this time I couldn't even fake a smile. This time when he said it I understood it to mean one of two things. He was either discriminating against me coz of the area I was from, or he didn't like me coz I was black. But I couldn't prove it. So I decided to stop cleaning tables when the restaurant was very busy one Saturday night. Even some of the waiters and kitchen staff said that I was right to stand up for myself. When Derek found out what I was doing he called me into his office. He was red in the face. He looked me straight in the eye and said, "What's going on?"

"It's to do with the promotion I've been asking for."

He asked me to get back to work and promised that we would sit down to discuss it later in the week.

The following Saturday I arrived at work early. I started cleaning and setting up the tables in the restaurant while the first customers for the day were being seated. Derek walked past me with two police officers and they went straight into his office.
Cool, I won't disturb him now. But when he's not busy I will remind him about our meeting.

I kept myself busy and carried on cleaning tables. A few minutes later Derek and the officers came out of his office and made their way towards me. I had my back to them, cleaning, when I felt the familiar cold steel of handcuffs on my wrist. "Robyn Travis, you are under arrest for theft."
"What?" Was this some joke?

I saw a group of white customers shake their heads as if to say, 'Typical'. I was shocked, embarrassed and angry at the same time.

"I didn't teef nuffin!" I shouted. "Derek, tell them." Derek wouldn't look me in the eyes. He turned his face. That's when I clocked that he was behind the Accusation. What a pussyhole.

I wanted to attack him but I didn't want to be seen as the stereotypical aggressive black boy. I held it down and didn't make a scene, and kept my head down as I was escorted out by the two officers. When they put me in the back of the van, I said, "Officer, that man don't like me. I didn't do nuffin." They both laughed and said, "Whatever, mate, we got you on CCTV."

"Yeah? Is it? I can't wait to see it."

At Soho police station I was searched then checked in. The desk sergeant asked, "What's he in for then?"

"Theft at work," one of the officers replied.

The sergeant turned to me.

"Why would you steal from your own work place?" Even he believed I'd done it.

They put me in a cell and left me in a state of confusion. I started to question whether I did do it or not. It was playing with my sanity. I punched the cell door out of anger and frustration. Hours later my solicitor came and I was interviewed then charged. I was bailed and told to return to Hammersmith court at a later date. This also meant that I lost my job.
I left the station filled with rage. I went to my Nan's and told her what happened. She told me to calm down and not to be mad, that they're probably racist. I loved Nan to bits. She didn't question me. She knew I didn't do it.

I went back to my B&B. Still angry. So angry, I couldn't breathe right. I built a bedtime spliff and stared at the photo of my dad that mum had given me. I smoked and stared at the snapshot for two hours straight. Then I took my lighter and set it alight. I watched as it slowly burned. I threw the ashes out the window, depressed that I didn't have a father to guide me through these crazy times. I was so mad.

I rolled out of bed, ran out the building and jumped on my moped. I wanted to take my anger out on any Fields boy I laid eyes on. After an hour of riding around with no particular place to go, I headed back to the B&B. With no photo of my dad I was already starting to forget what he looked like. I began to regret burning it. If he's really alive, how will I now recognise him? Mad with emotions I decided to smoke myself to sleep.

A month had passed since my arrest for theft. I went to court with my Nan and my solicitor. While we were waiting for my case to be called, Derek, the manager, walked in and sat a few feet away from us. Nan gave him a dirty look.

"You didn't do it, did you?" she whispered to me.

"No, Nan," I laughed.

She gave Derek another dirty look. The usher called my case and we walked into the court room. Derek swore on the Bible and accused me of theft. Then the evidence from the CCTV was shown. I finally got to see what I was accused of doing.

The guy on the CCTV had his back to the camera. He opened the office door, went straight into Derek's jacket pocket and stole his wallet. He then turned and we finally saw his face.

I burst out laughing. And I couldn't stop. The guy on the CCTV didn't look nothing like me. He just happened to be black. The judge couldn't take it seriously either. "Stop this nonsense," he shouted. "Get this mockery out of my court. NOT GUILTY!"

I was laughing but I was still angry. Derek had tried to frame me. I wanted to punch his face in, but Nan gave me one of those looks that she gave Derek. I would never disrespect my Nan like that or let her see the violent side of me. Of all the times I have been to court, this was the first time the judge was on my side. That didn't change the fact that I didn't get justice. I lost my job and self esteem all coz I asked for promotion. I lost my trust too and didn't feel like putting myself in the same situation again. I had so much other stress to deal with that I decided to put this one to the back of my mind. For now.

REVENGE AIN'T SWEET

April 2001 was a month of revenge and tears. Wayne Henry, 19, and Corey Wright, 20, from Hackney, were gunned down. The rumours were that it was the Tottenham boys.

These murders should have had no effect on me whatsoever. Wayne and Corey were older Fields boys. Fields boys were my enemies but I wasn't celebrating the news of their murders.

Tottenham boys don't like my brother either. What if they killed him? I'd have to roll out.

I felt it for the ones who lost their brothers. If I was in their shoes I would have been heartbroken and under pressure to avenge my brother's death. I couldn't tell anyone what I was really thinking. So when the Holly Street boys spoke about it, some of us would say simply, "That's how it goes on the streets." In the back of my mind I was wondering if they felt the same way I did about the murders. The streets had turned me cold but it didn't stop me having a heart. Road life wasn't just black and white. Because it also didn't change the fact that I was still planning to kill Kane.

A month later it was time for my GCSE exams. I don't even know why I bothered to show up for some of them coz I knew nothing about anything. After five years in three different schools and a pupil referral unit, I couldn't tell anyone what I had learned. Moving from school to school made it impossible to keep up with what was being taught. I pretended not to care coz I knew I was going to fail. Deep down I wanted to pass with flying colours. On the day of my English exam, me and my boy Dudus smoked a big skunk spliff then bopped into the exam hall. We arrived late, stunk of weed, and we were both high. And, surprise-surprise - we both failed miserably.

A few weeks after, on the final school day, we were presented with our national record of achievement (NRA) in the assembly hall. I wasn't going to bother turning up coz I knew I hadn't achieved nothing. But my brother and Clint encouraged me to go and said that they would come with me. When we arrived, the whole of Year 11 were sitting with their parents.

I was glad I didn't invite my Nan coz there was nothing for me to celebrate. The head of year Ms. Parry called the names of the students. One by one they went on stage to collect their folders. I was waiting for ages for my name to be called when Ms. Parry said, "That's all folks, thanks for coming. No, I'm only joking - Robyn Travis..."

I was relieved to at least get a folder of achievement. But there was only one piece of paper in the whole folder. The paper said I got French level one and double G in science. Rah! What a waste of five years in education.

Later that evening the Year 11s had a boat party on the River Thames. I went to celebrate and say goodbye to my year mates. I spent most of the boat trip smoking weed and getting twisted. On the way home on the coach, different teachers came over to me, saying they knew I was living a hectic life and had no support. They said I was smart and that I shouldn't let my GCSE results determine my future. Even though I was twiss-up I began to think, these teachers must be as drunk as I am if they really believe I'm smart.

--

School life was over. I had no qualifications and no job. Restless and stressed, wondering what my next step in life would be, I went over to Holly Street to see a close bredrin. I told him what I was going through. He told me his problems. For the first time we had a real heart to heart. He gave me a spliff from the ashtray.

I took two draws from it and screwed up my face. "Oi, bruv, what the fuck is this?"

"It's my old man's, it's crack." I gave him a dirty look. For some reason he found it funny. I couldn't understand why one of my friends would give me crack at one of my lowest moments. Who needs enemies when you've got friends like mine.

It wasn't the only snakey thing he had done to me, but it was the worst. Crack had ruined my family and it seemed like he didn't care if it ruined me as well. Weeks later I was jamming on the block with da mandem when someone said our so-called bredrin was a crack head. A few of them laughed and joked about it. I couldn't allow them to talk about him like that. " 'Llow dem talk," I said. "He ain't no crack head. Are you lot stupid?"

Our bredrin turned up in the middle of the conversation and heard what was being said about him. He looked like he had too much on his mind to even bother defending himself.

Holly Street didn't have the most caring people. In time of need, some would run joke at your expense. Like that shit was funny. Whether the rumours were true or not I wasn't going to turn my back on my bredrin through this bad patch. We all had our low points.

Weeks later, I went to the doctors for my hay fever. "You don't look your usual self, Mr. Travis. Are you okay?"

"Yeah, I know. I've been really stressed recently." Thinking about it, I'd been finding it hard to laugh these days.

"I've looked at your records and it looks like there's a lot going on with you. I want you to start taking these tablets. They will make you feel better."

I went back to my nasty B&B, rolled a spliff and took two tablets. I was buzzing differently, thinking about all the drama of the past year. Stabbed. A gun put to my head. Evicted. Put into care. Accused of theft. Sacked. Failed at school. And the possibility that my Dad faked his death.

I read the label on the bottle of tablets. 'Anti depressants'. I had no idea what that meant. Over a period of taking them, I noticed that my temper grew shorter. When I was happy, I laughed until I cried. It was like the medication gave my laughter more joy and my temper more venom. Maybe the combination of skunk and the anti-depressants was turning me into a mad man. I felt like a walking health hazard. Life wasn't just hard, it was crazy.

It was around this time that I started walking with a knife every day. It was also around this time that I got my first gun. I wasn't loud about it and I didn't feel right in myself but extreme environment calls for extremes measures.

One hot day in July me and a couple mandem were cotching on the block. Brendan, another boy from the ends, came and said some boys down the road had troubled him. I didn't know what the passa was about, but me, Brendan and a next guy, Likkle Vicious jumped in a rusty car and went looking for them. When we pulled up Brendan pointed out who had chucked it to him - three big African guys, older than us. I wasn't on no long ting. I bopped up and bored-up the biggest one in his chest a few times. The other two ran off. We chased them but couldn't catch them, so we jumped into the car and went back to Holly Street. Soon after some African boys came back to roll on us. As soon as I clocked the pattern I ran up to their car, dragged out the driver and began to stab and kick him.

Then Risky-Talent and a few of the Holly Street boys came over and rushed the other guys. God knows why I backed Brendan's beef coz he wasn't even really my friend like that. I mean, we grew up in the same area but I had never even stepped foot in my boy's house. The problem was I was shorter-tempered; I didn't feel I needed anyone to back me, and I was angry at every injustice in my life - that was my excuse for wilding out. I felt regret before I got back home. Coz of my renk temper my circle of enemies got bigger.

Days later me and Marcus bopped out of the Chinese shop on

Queensbridge to see some older boy standing there giving us man some stink screw face.

"Wot's your problem, blud?" Marcus asked the boy. I didn't care what his problem was. I put my special fried rice down, it was a laid-back thing, walked up to him and threw my piping hot sweet and sour in his face. He was covered in it. Screaming. I sparked him in the face, then we stamped him out. "Oh my god, Robyn... Sweet and sour sauce?" Marcus laughed as we bopped back to the Chinese for replacement sweet and sour. "You're moving reckless."

It was extreme but I couldn't control this temper. And I didn't have heart left to care. It was nothing personal. I just wanted to share my pain with the world, and anyone who chucked it to me.

At this point I didn't have many real friends. As I said, I took my friendship with the click seriously and was committed to do almost anything for them. But they didn't seem committed to me. Marcus alone had left me for dead twice. Our friendship seemed fake. I slowly began to distance myself from a few of the team coz they kept doing dodgy things that real friends ain't supposed to do. I struggled to come to terms with it. I was starting to feel like a mug and couldn't handle being let down again.

I became closer to Darker and Mintz coz they said they were the only ones who had my back when I got stabbed. I had my doubts. If they had my back how the hell could they have walked away from the beef without a scratch? Considering there was so many Fields boys with weapons. Nevertheless, I never questioned Darker about what he said, maybe coz I didn't want to face the uncomfortable truth.

I became less close with Geezer and I stopped talking to Marcus altogether. We had a few arguments and, when we saw each other, I cussed him for being such a fake friend. My patience grew thin. I got tired of the arguing and wanted to fight instead. But he never wanted it. He couldn't understand why I got so angry. I was just fed up of fake friends around me - full stop.

A GLIMPSE OF HOPE

August 2001. I went to see my Nan and had some Sunday dinner. She seemed really concerned about my living habits and was aware that I was smoking weed. She said I wasn't the same Robyn. I had to agree with her. Circumstances (and maybe the cocktail of skunk and anti-depressants) had changed me.

Nan had a surprise for me. She was moving back to her old place in Holly Street and me and my brother would be coming with her. This news gave me a reason to smile and a sense of hope. I felt relieved. I was going back to some normal family life. We moved in a few days later. The whole house had been decorated. It felt like home. Nan encouraged me to go to college in September and I agreed.

I was so happy to be back where I could eat soul food instead of McDonalds. The company of my Nan and my brother made me want to stay indoors most of the time. I didn't want to bring any drama to her house. Living at my Nan's I had to behave a certain way anyway. I couldn't smoke and it wasn't a cotching spot for my friends like my place had always been. Even my selection of music changed. It wouldn't have been right to blast hardcore rap in my Nan's face. So instead of da mandem coming round to hear me tump Nas, Mega, Nori, DMX and Mobb Deep, I had girls coming to link me to the sounds of Jagged Edge. I got rid of my gun, knife and my hot-head behaviour and I was no longer on anti-depressants. I also decided not to spend all my time in Hackney like some prisoner. My world was bigger than that. The postcode beef wouldn't stop me from going where I wanted to. I soon enrolled in City & Islington College, without the belief that I could achieve anything. So the only thing I studied was the girls.

It was halloween 2001. Nan's birthday. She sent me to the shop. As I was walking through the estate I saw a few of the guys throwing eggs at each other. It looked fun so I joined in. I took two eggs off this boy and threw one at him and his friends. Then I walked up to a boy pretended to throw the other egg at him. As it was cold, I was wearing my cotton gloves and I lost grip of the egg. It slipped out of my hand and hit him in the face. I didn't think it was that bad coz he had a mask on, but some of it went on his clothes. I said "sorry", I was only ramping. Everyone was laughing and he probably felt embarrassed. He got brave and grabbed me. I said sorry "but if you don't let go, then boy... yuh nah." He wouldn't listen so I pushed him.

Marcus decided to get involved coz the boy was his girlfriend's little brother. He probably felt he needed to play hero. He screwed up his face. "Pick on someone your own size?" he said. I was baffled. All of a sudden he wanted to play bad bwoy coz it was his girlfriend's brother. What a joker.

Marcus was a year older than me and, like Mohammed, looked older than his age. He was over six feet with plenty of facial hair. He grabbed me and I grabbed him back. We continued to grab each other until we ended up around the corner from his house, my back up against the wall. "You're a pussy! A pussy," Marcus was shouting.

I completely froze, I could see his mouth moving, but I couldn't hear him. Then I had a flashback. I was in the same place, on the same spot, a year and a half earlier with a gun to my head for defending Marcus.

Hold on. Is this the same guy who ran off and left me for dead when I got stabbed backing his beef? The same guy who, when I phoned him and told him I had a gun pointed to my head coz of him, was crying down the phone like a baby, too scared to come back? Now he's calling ME a pussy? He must have lost his mind.

"Come round the corner in five minutes," I told him. "I'm gonna change into my tracksuit then we can fight properly. Just me and you.

No crowd. No hype." Marcus didn't back down and continued to run his mouth, so I knew it was on.

I went back to my Nan's, feeling happy and angry at the same time. Happy coz I knew I would get to let my anger out on this guy for being such a fake friend over the years. And angry coz he had the cheek to call me a pussy after all I had done for him. I changed my clothes and went in the front room where my Nan and Aunty Dee were sitting. I was in a rage but I didn't want Nan to see. Especially on her birthday. I put on a fake smile and gave Nan the change and the drink I bought from the shop. I then left and went out to fight. The moment I stepped outside I saw Marcus and Lips walking towards me. I thought Marcus was trying to be smart by bringing our friend Lips to my house to squash the beef. But I wasn't interested in squashing anything. I was too angry for peace talks. This had been building up for a long time.

"Let's go in the Holly Street cage and fight," I said. Marcus looked at Lips. "See what I mean, he's crazy," Marcus said. It seemed like he wanted to back out. I couldn't understand why. Ten minutes earlier he was on it. I noticed a kitchen knife up his sleeve. It looked big enough to cut joints in a butcher's shop. I was shocked, confused and surprised.

"What's up your sleeve, bruv? What's that up your sleeve? A knife, yeah? Is that for me, yeah?" I said. "Who's that for, Marcus? For me? Aight, bad man, wait there."

He didn't answer. He just stood in silence, looking guilty as if to say, Shit! Robyn's clocked. What now? I was so angry. Someone who was once my best friend, a person I put my life on the line for, was bringing a knife to use on me. And hiding it too. I never knew he could be so sneaky. What a fucking snake.

I went back inside to get the biggest knife in the yard, but I couldn't find it. Then I looked in the front room to see that the knife was in my Nan's birthday cake. I went back to the kitchen and picked up a butter knife. No way was I going to diss my Nan by taking the big knife out of the cake in front of her.

"Robyn, you alright?" Nan said in her Bajan accent. "Yes Nan, I'm fine." I fake-smiled and tucked the butter knife up my sleeve. I hated having to lie but I didn't want to bring my street life anywhere near her. Part of me wished I had kept my knife and gun when I moved in with her.

I stepped out and told Marcus and Lips to come round the corner. I didn't want a fight outside my Nan's house. Neither of them moved. "You got your big knife and I got my little joke of a knife," I said to Marcus. "Let's go in the cage and stab each other up. Whoever survives is the winner." He laughed nervously. I could see in his eyes that he wasn't ready for this level of beef. I picked up on a vibe that he was torn between pride and fear. But he gave the impression that he wasn't scared. "Move from my Nan's house or I'm gonna bore you up," I said. He blanked me. And that didn't help my temper. "I'll count to ten, and if you don't move then 'blam'. One, two..."

Marcus didn't seem to take me seriously he started to laugh. So I flipped and stabbed him a few times in the neck and head. I wanted to do serious damage coz his knife was so big in comparison to mine. My flimsy knife broke, so I ran upstairs to get my baseball bat to finish him. When I got back downstairs, my Nan and Aunty Dee were at the front door. It sounded like someone was trying to kick it down from the outside. Nan and Aunty Dee assumed that people were after me. They panicked and were about to call the police.

"No, don't call the police," I said. "I stabbed one of 'em." Just the thought of Marcus kicking Nan's door made me want to take the big knife out of the cake and duppy him. Nan and Aunty Dee stood at the door to stop me from going back out. So I focused on trying to calm them down instead. Disrespecting my Nan in her house on her birthday wasn't part of my plan. I'd let my rage get the better of me again.
I was still angry and frustrated and wanted to go back out to finish what I had started. I went up to my bedroom and was tempted to jump out of the window, but I couldn't fit through it. A lot of people were outside watching the drama. I heard Geezer shout, "How could you stab him?" The way he said it, gave me the impression that he was on Marcus's side.

What a fool. If he was a true friend he would've known there was a good enough reason for me to take it to that level. I was still looking through the window when I saw Geezer and some others rush to put Marcus in a car, taking him to hospital.

My brother came home shortly after. I told him what had happened. He said Marcus deserved it for bringing a knife to me in the first place. He was more angry to hear that Marcus kicked down my Nan's door. A few hours later Marcus' aunt knocked my Nan's door to ask questions about what happened. She knew that me and Marcus were once friends. As she was talking to my brother and my Nan, I heard someone making up noise in a car outside. I couldn't believe my ears. It was Marcus running up his gums.

My brother stopped being polite to his Aunty and ran out to the car. By the time I got there he was already kicking Marcus in the head. Marcus was screaming his head off. We tried to pull Marcus out of the car but it drove off before we got the chance. This is a mad ting. Me and my brother backed this boy's beef so many times. What the fuck possessed him to bring a knife? This prick's lucky, I could've killed him. That's a madness. I could've duppied one of da mandem.

Oh well, I would have had to live with that nightmare. Certain man are snakes. Bare funny moves ah gwarn round 'ere. Whatever happened to da mandem backing each other and that? No homo or nutt'n but I thought da mandem would stick together through any passa, in sickness and health, for richer or for poorer, and all that death do us part malarkey.

I couldn't sleep that night, feeling guilty that my Nan witnessed a side of me I was trying to hide from her. The fact that my aunt stayed over in my Nan's room made me really think about how my hotheaded actions affect others. Although my Nan tried to hide her disappointment in me, I felt it and hated myself for letting her down.

A couple weeks later I came home from college and was waiting for my Nan to come back from Asda in Leyton. She had gone out with her little trolley to do some shopping. Living with her was 'shabby'.

She always cooked me and my brother a proper meal, dinner was always there for me. That day she cooked rice and peas with lamb chops. I shared out a plate but I couldn't finish it, so I saved the rest for later. A couple hours passed and Nan still hadn't returned. I was watching TV when my brother came in my bedroom. "Nan's just had a heart attack. She's in hospital but don't watch that, she'll be a'right," he said.

I went on my knees and prayed. Fuck sake, man. Why now? Two years earlier she had a heart attack on my birthday, just after wishing me the best for the day. She was in a coma but pulled through that one. So I tried not to think the worst. We waited for someone to ring and tell us what was going on but we never got that call. My brother said, "Bun da long ting, we're going to the hospital."

We jumped in his car and drove to Whipps Cross. We asked the receptionist at A&E and she told us which ward my Nan was in. When we got to the ward, my uncle was there. He called me and my brother into a room. He had this vex look on his face. "She's on life support and she ain't got long left," he said. When he said that my heart skipped a beat. I wasn't interested in why he was vex. I just wanted to see Nan. I refused to believe she would die. I walked in to see her lying unconscious with tubes in her nose and arms. The whole family was by her bedside, except for mum, who I hadn't seen for a year. No one had her number to phone her.

I held Nan's hand. I whispered how much I loved her and told her I would come back in the morning. I swear I felt her hand move. I prayed silently for a miracle, then me and my brother went home.

The next morning came and there was no word about Nan. I was bless with that coz no news is good news. I got dressed to go to the hospital and as I was brushing my teeth, I felt a hand on my shoulder. "Sorry, bruv... Nan just died," my brother said. I said, "Cool."

I knew he must have been upset for himself and for me, coz he never showed me any comfort, like a hand on the shoulder, when we were growing up. He left me in the bathroom to brush my teeth. That's when it hit. I collapsed and cried like a baby. I couldn't believe it. The one person who had never turned their back on me, who never left me hungry or for dead was now gone forever. The one person who gave me a sense of hope was now in Heaven. Gone.

My brother came back in, picked me up, and we smoked some weed to help deal with the pain. I weren't crying any more. We smoked all day, but it didn't help. Food didn't even cross my mind.

I couldn't sleep so I went into Nan's room. It was flooded with flashbacks of her quoting Psalms in her Bajan accent, and warning me to stay away from "all ah dese fass gurls", as she wasn't ready to be a great grandmother just yet. The flashbacks did my head in.

My plate of leftover food from the day before was waiting downstairs. I warmed it up and sat down to eat, digesting the fact that this was the last time I would ever taste Nan's cooking. Every spoonful reminded me of another sweet memory of her. It took over an hour to eat that small plate of food, fighting hard to hold back the tears. Someone eventually got hold of my mum and told her the tragic news. It wasn't said directly, but some in the family blamed me for Nan's death. They believed that what triggered her heart attack was me stabbing Marcus on her doorstep.

Two weeks later we buried the head of our family and the queen of my heart. Mum was at the funeral. I thought about hugging her but I was too angry to show emotions or tears. We met soon after, but we weren't able to sort out our differences so we went our separate ways and got on with our lives. The family didn't seem to be getting along, so when it came to Nan's possessions there were family politics about who kept what. I felt a vibe towards me of anger and blame. I understood their feelings but they weren't respecting Nan's wishes. Just weeks before my Nan died me and my brother sat in her room and she said, "If anything ever happens to me I want you to have this roof over your head." Unfortunately her words no longer seemed to count.

A few weeks later I was homeless again. I asked my Auntys if I could sleep on the floor at their houses until I sorted something out. But they all said "no". I guess me and my brother weren't flavour of the month. We were left to fend for ourselves.

After a few weeks of sleeping here and there I went back to my social worker. She told me that I was going to be put in shared accommodation until I was eighteen years old, then I would get my own flat. Just my luck. Chups! They had to go an' re-house me in E8. Clarence Road of all places. How the fuck could my social workers house me in Pembury with all my enemies? I can't be mad at them, doh, they didn't know any better. This street ting is my problem not theirs. It's not like I'm going to tell them, "No, please, don't house me there, I've got beef with dem Pembury man".

I wasn't even there a week before they clocked me. I was chatting to a Pembury girl called Carmella outside the Caribbean shop on Clarence Road when she told me what was gwarning. "Robyn, I don't think dem man across the road like you, y'know." I looked over my shoulder and saw bare enemies standing across the road. They probably thought that I came for beef but they had no idea that I was now resident in Pembury. I put my arm around Carmella to style it out like she was my link. And that probably wound them up even more coz all da mandem in Hackney thought she was peng.

"Don't let anyone know I'm living here," I told her. "I'm just gonna keep my head down and get on with things and hopefully nothing don't kick off between me and dem man deh."

With Nan gone I gave up college and was thinking of looking for a nine to five to survive, when the streets reminded me about the last time I tried to go legit.

VOICE OF THE STREETS: Job? Are you for real, bruv? You done tried this working ting already. It's not for you, G. You're a black boy from the hood with no qualifications. Do you think anyone's gonna take you on with that record? You're a road man. Stick to the fuckin' script.

VOICE OF REASON: Look for a job. That's the right ting. Your mum never raised no fool. And you know your Nan would want better for you.

VOICE OF THE STREETS: Bruv, Kane's still walking around and

you're talking about getting a job. You're acting like you're not on this ting any more. In fact ... nah, nah, get a job. At least that way when we kill Kane they won't suspect us coz you earn an- 'honest' living. Yeah, do that, bruv. That idea's sick.

I got a nightshift job cleaning trains in Lewisham. The work was just as hard as cleaning tables at the restaurant. I picked up litter and cleaned people's mess and scrubbed graffiti off the train carriages. After holding the job down for a few months, I got fed up and quit.

A week before I quit I was at the station going home from work. It was around seven in the morning and I was on the platform waiting for my train. There were a few other people in suits on the platform going to work. I looked around and saw my old manager, Derek, from the restaurant. When he saw me he went red in the face. I began to think about what he did.

If only this man gave me the promotion I had asked for and didn't get me fired from my job in the restaurant. I would've never had the time to get caught back up in the streets. I would've stacked up a lot of money by now. Maybe my life would be different.

"Derek, why did you lie to get me fired? You fucked my life up."

"I'm really sorry, Robyn," he said. "I really thought it was you who robbed me."

I'm from the streets so I know when somebody's chattin' shit. But I clocked he was terrified of what my next move was going to be. I honestly wanted to kick him onto the train tracks, but I could hear my Nan's voice saying, "Robyn, just forgive him." The train came at the same time. So I just kissed my teeth, got on and went home.

LIVIN' ON ENEMY TURF

By the time I moved to Clarence Road, Holly Street wasn't the same place for me. I had a funny feeling that there was more hate than love for me there so I began to slowly distance myself. I stopped hanging with the Holly Street boys and became a lone soldier. At times I would par with the Paid in Full mandem from Clapton Square, Top-Shotta and Bayders. Dem man were the hood stars in Square. Sadly, too many brothers had fallen victim to that strip. E5 became known as the "murder mile". Even by the media.

By now I only had patience for mandem who I genuinely had love for. I had to have at least 80% faith that they would play their role if beef went down. For me and many others on the street, friendship was based on who's there for you, and that included having your boy's back, no matter what. I personally saw it as a way of showing love and 'keeping it real'. For most peeps on the streets, when someone had your back it created a silent special bond. For some of us that bond was like a life insurance policy. That's why I didn't mind parring with dem Square man. They showed me love and were ready to have my back when it came to the Fields boys. I respected Top-Shotta and Bayders and saw them as REAL brothers. But even though we became tight, I still wasn't 100% certain that they had my back to the end. Like Bayders himself would say, "There's too many fake-arse Suge Knights out 'ere nowadays."

Taking Kane out was still high on my agenda. He was my main target when it came to rolling on the Fields boys. But my experiences with certain Holly Street man fucked me up. I couldn't tell who was real and who wasn't. When it came down to it, I realised that the only person I could depend on one hundred percent, in beef, was ME.

Trust is a luxury I can't afford. Betrayal's something I can't ignore. If I'm honest, I didn't even know what the full meaning of 'keeping it real' was any more. I assumed it meant always back da mandem's beef, never snitch, never touch your bredrin's wifey and never snake man. I couldn't understand why most of da mandem I parred with found it so hard to maintain these simple guidelines. It's not like Holly Street boys were pussies. Not even. It's just that they got shook to back the beef whenever we were outnumbered or the other team had olders. We never had no olders backing us. They all went when the flats got knocked down.

At this time I found a lot of realness and comfort in listening to NY rapper Cormega. His tunes had me in a zone, especially when I had a spliff to hand. My favourite album at this time had to be: Cormega 'The Realness'. I could listen to that album from the first track all the way through. The interlude alone had me pullin up the track over and over.

It was now march 2002, I was seventeen years old and still living on my own. Very few brothers in general were keeping it 100% real out 'ere. But every now and then someone who was from a next part of Hackney would surprise me. Like the time when I got given a gun from a next road man. I didn't even have to ask for it. Man just clocked that my situation on Pembury was sticky, he had drama with dem Pembury boys himself and so he decided to 'show love'. Free of charge. I rolled with that strap daily. I hardly went anywhere without it. I had to stay on my Ps and Qs cah dem Pembury boys had a big crew who linked up tight with the Fields boys. Shit! That's a lot of enemies - Holly Street, Fields and Pembury. Not to mention certain Tottenham man.

After a while I started to feel a touch more at ease living in P Block. Especially, when I had da ting on me. Though I was a swingers and what not, nuff breddahs weren't fighting fair more. Tell ah lie, peeps weren't fighting full stop.
A few weeks after I got my second gun, I got caught in a madness

again. Chups! Am I under some sort of street curse or something? Why am I always outnumbered? This time the passa wasn't with the usual suspects, it was with some of dem Stamford Hill man. I was bopping down Clarence Road when two boys rode towards me on super bikes. Looking cold with it. Braap! Dem bikes look shabby.

Little did I know they were planning to move to me. I kept it moving. As I was crossing one of the boys revved up for attention but I paid him no mind. He stalled the bike and I laughed, going about my business. On Mare Street Narrow Way one of the bikes rode past. I turned to see the other brudder close up giving face. He had a bullet proof vest on and was obviously feeling boasy about himself. He took off the helmet and started chatting some shit.

Real talk, I didn't have time for the hype talk. This beef wasn't even mine, I inherited it. I never had beef with dem Stamford Hill lot. They had their passa with the Holly Street B team. I got involved by accident. I tried to break up the beef and a man confused me for one of them and so I had to take it to him.

Halfway through the gangsta talk I said, "Eff the long talk, bruv, let's go to the graveyard and swing it out." Then he started talking greazy 'bout, "Nah Rob, it's a different era it's a gun ting now."

"Cool, shoot me then," I said. Passers-by looked on. They could feel the tension. The other boy came over on his bike. He also had a vest. We was good to go. Then the feds came.

"What's going on here?"

"Nothing officer," I said. "Everything's bless. We're just reasoning." They knew I was lying but man never snitch. Not even on enemies. Standard procedure. When the police left, the boy said, "Safe for that, Rob."

We touched fist and kept it moving. He probably thought I was doing him a favour coz he was strapped, but the dude had no idea that my gun was off safety sitting in my waist. I was never impressed by gun talk, coz we all bleed red.

I really felt like I was cursed on the streets coz if it weren't one madness, it was another. The Pembury boys used to see me in their area all the time and I still weren't sure if they had clocked why they kept seeing me strolling through so often. I could feel a vibe in the air. Like, they were sick of seeing man's face or sutt'n'. From where they were standing it probably looked like I was 'dissin the programme', boppin through their endz like I could take on all of Pembury.

Did I think I was badder than all dem Pembury man? Nope. Not even. I might have acted like I didn't give a fuck about them or their area, coz I felt I had to go on wicked. Bottom line, they were tight with Fields which made them my enemies. More girls from Pembury warned me that certain man didn't like my character. Pembury boys didn't know my character, they only heard the name. They didn't give a shit, they just saw me as Holly Street in their endz. They didn't understand I was a lone soldier.

One time I left my hostel to go to the corner shop on Clarence. I looked up and saw at least thirty Pembury boys jammin on a long balcony. One of them, Shotty, was giving me some proper screw face then he started hyping. I told him to wait until I bopped back home and returned fully loaded. I wasn't going to get caught slippin'. Last time I was in a similar situation I got stabbed.

I was all alone and ready to ride or die for my name's sake. And, seeing as they saw me as a Holly Street boy, I had to rep that. I felt like I had no choice but to rep. Out of nowhere one of the older Pembury mandem shouted, "Whose likkle brudder are you?" I told him who my brother was. "I know your big brudder still," he said. That was no comfort. I knew my brother wasn't friends with many people from Pembury. "'Llow it, this beef is long," the Pembury older said. "Robyn's a real yute, you lot should link up and squash the beef. We're all Hackney man anyway."

His words calmed things down. He told me not to be so hot-headed with da mandem coz we need to stick together. Especially as things between Hackney and Tottenham were getting serious. He talked about the beef between Hackney and Tottenham. He said he was there when the Hackney boys killed Popcorn. I don't know why he was telling me this. I couldn't figure out whether he was bragging or what. Whatever his gameplay, I wasn't interested in who done what to who.

Growing up, many olders told me similar stories about how and why the beef started between Hackney and Tottenham. I never really took on what they were saying. For some reason, that day I did. But to be told that they fell out over 'money movements' made the war seem pointless coz everyone was friends in the first place. Who knows the truth? I know there were always little pockets of beef between Hackney and Totty man but from my eyes it got serious with the death of Popcorn. I thought of all the times I had heard people from Hackney or Tottenham saying they wanted to get involved in the beef, when many of them didn't even know what it was all about. The sad truth is that this beef forced young black boys to hate and kill other young black boys they didn't even know. Anyway, from that day on, me and the Pembury boys were bless - to some extent.

Back at the hostel I started thinking how crazy life was. Fifteen minutes earlier I was willing to shoot any Pembury boy who tried to rush me. Now we were cool and had mutual respect for each other. It was way too easy to kill or be killed or go to prison, especially when you're living with too much pride on these streets. Way too easy. Some people would say I was brave or 'keeping it real', and to some extent I would have to agree. I might have been brave, but my actions were hot-headed and foolish at the same time.

--

I was beginning to get used to living in Pembury without watching my back so hard. Heading towards Clarence Road for some Caribbean food one day, I buss'd the corner and walked into a riot between Pembury boys and boi-dem. My heart was racing. What shall I do? The police were my real enemies but I didn't want to help out the Pembury boys coz I didn't want the streets to think I was begging friends with them. The police treated them like shit with CS gas and batons. It was fuckries.

Whenever the police hit one of them I felt it. I saw an officer hit a woman and I began to see red. I still wasn't sure if this battle was mine to fight. Some of the Pembury boys were reppin and putting up a good fight, but they were outnumbered and nuff ah them got arrested. After the riot I went back to the hostel. I felt ashamed. I questioned my decision not to help. I felt like a sellout. All coz I was worried that the streets would see me as a Holly Street boy who switched.

I later found out that the woman who was hit was Shotty's mum and that he was sent to prison for attacking the policeman who punched her. I felt Shotty's pain. My heart went out to his people. Even though we had our differences, I was vex to hear that his mum was assaulted by boi-dem. I was even angrier to hear that he went to prison for defending her. In my eyes, Shotty kept it real.

Most of my life I have been beefing with black boys who look just like me and have similar struggles to me. We hated each other just coz we lived in different postcodes. I was beginning to realise that our fight wasn't with each other and that our common enemy was the police.

FRIENDS WITH A FIELDS BOY

It had almost been a year now since my Nan died, and I still wasn't doing anything constructive with my life. I was still broke but refused to be the stereotypical drug dealer. Instead, I enrolled in Shoreditch College to do a sports course. Like my Nan would have wanted me to. Shoreditch College was a hot spot for me. Most of the Holly Street and Fields boys went there. I was put in the same class as Jadie, the only Fields boy I had time for. I still had mixed emotions about Holly Street. So I kept myself to myself.

It was strange seeing Fields and Holly Street boys in the common room and no beef kicking off. It made me start to wonder if I was the troublemaker. Everyone else at college was getting on with their lives whereas in my mind I was trapped in the beef I inherited. Still a prisoner to the streets.

I got back into football. I joined the college team. I wasn't the same player I used to be coz of all the weed I was smoking, but I was still good enough to be the first choice striker. I played up front with Wildcat, and a few other Fields boys including Nedz and Jadie. Even though I had beef with the majority of the boys in the team, I never let that affect the way I played. And I can't deny it, our team was hot. Imagine if we never wasted all this time beefing over foolishness, and took football more seriously growing up. Some of us could be playing Premier League, no doubt.

It was good to see Jadie again. Peeps wondered who would win a fight, but it just weren't like that between us. We had similar mindsets and a lot in common. Don't get it twisted, we were both prisoners to the streets still, but Jadie was a cool brudder. Just what the streets needed - a guy who had sense out 'ere and wasn't afraid to think differently from the rest. Anybody who thought like Jadie did at that young age, was almost guaranteed a ticket out of this vicious street mentality.

One time me and Jadie were sitting in the classroom giving each other some half hearted screw face when he said, "Robyn, you Holly Street boys have got the best screw face in Hackney." I tried not to laugh but J was a kid who knew how to break the ice in any awkward moment. It reminded me of the first time I met him way back when I was in Year 5. We used to run so many jokes on the pitch at training as well. It was ridiculous. But after the jokes we got serious. Halfway through the lesson he showed me how he felt about the beef between me and his boy Kane, "Rob, you getting stabbed was fuckery. Cah me and you go way back. Worse still you and Kane was bredrins those times, and he's still my bredrin all now. Rah! This is too technical, yah know. Best if you two just squash the beef if you can, cah it's long fam".

I explained to Jadie that even though he and some other Fields mandem had kept it real and stayed mutual, Kane's stabbing me like a piece of shit, messed me up. Forget the physical pain, it was the head fuck. We spoke on a big boy level that day, then began talking friendly again, just like the old days.

No one from Holly Street or Fields could say anything. If they did, then it was behind our backs. Not long after, I dropped out of college again.

STILL A HOT-HEAD

I still had no real focus on what I wanted to do with my life. I felt like a complete waste man. I couldn't see a way of becoming successful without selling drugs or going to college. But I didn't want to do either of the two. All I had going for me was that I had mad heart and courage, but none of that shit could pay my bills.

One day, my cousin Redz came to the hostel and told me he got jacked for his mobile by some Springfield boys. No long ting, I threw on my tracksuit and breezed out. Halfway down the road I realised I forgot to bring my gun. Redz was begging me not to go there without it coz there was nuff of them there. But I was like, "Cool cuz, I got this."

When it came to family, emotions often overcame my common sense. If truth be told, I didn't rate Springfield boys like I rated Fields and Pembury. When we got to 'Murder Mile', I saw about twelve Springfield boys standing in a group. I bopped up to them.

"Who jacked my cousin? Which bad bwoy jacked my cousin? If I don't get back my cousin's phone in exactly two minutes, I'm gonna stab man to bits." A few of the older boys in the crew tried to reason with me but I wasn't in a talking mood. Almost immediately they returned the phone. I sensed that a few of them didn't like my bad boy attitude, but they knew I was a wild hot-head that no one could tame.

Me and Redz went back to the hostel. I told him not to go round there, but if the Springfield boys bothered him, next time, my gun would do the talking. The older I got, the shorter my temper and general patience for guys on road became. I wanted to hurt anyone who violated the people I cared about. Weeks after that passa with Redz, my friend Od'z from T town phoned me. He said he and a couple of his boys got rushed in Finsbury Park by some Fields boys.

The second I heard that I acted on it. I went to where da mandem jam on the estate. I saw Jadie chilling on the block. He could see I wasn't in no jokey-smiley mood. I went straight up and questioned him. Jadie didn't know what went down but I didn't care. I wanted him to find the man who rushed Od'z so we could fight it out. I wasn't completely honest doh: I said I wanted to fight but my intentions were a lot worse. Jadie made some calls to his boys saying, "Robyn's here on our block ready to fight whoever rushed his cousin."

Every phone call Jadie made the response was the same. If they weren't there, they weren't coming to fight. Jadie came off the phone looking confused. "Rob, man are saying he's not even your cousin, he's just a Tottenham boy."

"Okay, he's not my cousin, but my bredrins are like fam. I don't care where they're from".

No one came to fight me, so me and Jadie just chilled on the block. Whilst we were chattin, Jadie asked me why I was always backing other people's beef. I told him that my boys are my boys. "But your boys don't have your back," he said. "Do you 'member that time at Palace Pavilion, when your bredrin Raiden was screw facing me? I saw him tap you on your shoulder and point at me. You were heading towards me, quick to back him on some hype ting when I smiled and pointed to show you that Raiden was walking away. You then stopped, shook your head, and went back to dance."

After the conversation with Jadie I went home to do some deep thinking about this street life. I thought about all the beef I'd ever had, or gotten myself into. It was hardly ever started coz of me. I was just always quick to jump in and defend 'my boys', 'my street' and 'my endz'. Weeks later it was still on my mind. I decided to work out who my real friends were, who I would ride or die for, and who I thought would ride or die for me.

I was jammin on the estate when I saw risky-talent and JJ talking in a car. JJ was my brother's age, but used to hang with da mandem even though he never backed any beef. Like many others he just enjoyed saying he was a Holly Street boy coz of the rep we had, but he never contributed to it.

Me and JJ started to talk. During the conversation he started to get cocky, which was out of character. Risky-Talent was laughing and stirring it as usual. JJ smiled and said, "Rob, why don't you get your money up or something? You're looking rough these days."

I couldn't believe he said that, but I had to admit it was true. I was looking rough. I was barely seventeen with no parents, no job and no one to ask for support. The cheek of it. This prick boy JJ is making jokes about me being broke when he's twenty years old and still living with mummy. He probably don't even pay no bills. Chups!

JJ and many others didn't understand that I chose to be broke. Let's be real, if I was a bad mind person or the jealous type I could've easily robbed him of the car he was sitting in. Or I could've robbed anyone else who was making money. It's not like anyone in Holly Street or Hackney had control or power over me. I was at an age where no one could stop me from getting my hustle on. My own brother couldn't stop me from dream chasing if I really wanted to. I could have stolen clientele from everyone in Holly Street who was in the game. The way I was - ride or die - at seventeen, no other Holly Street boy my age or older could have told me nothing. I had bare connects and I could have taken over my endz. But I didn't wanna 'get rich or die trying'.

Other than Darker, no one knew this side of me. The side which would work nine to five but still ride or die for Holly Street. The side which was up for a drive-by but refused to do a robbery. The side that refused to sell crack or heroin. I didn't want certain things on my conscience. I would rather hurt someone out of love for my friends, than hurt someone for financial gain.

Seeing JJ smile about my hardships made me lose it. I wanted to stab him up but lucky for the pussy, at that moment, I saw about forty Fields boys walking onto our estate. I left JJ to confront the Fields boys. I didn't have an ounce of fear in me coz I had my knife and I was already in a ready-for-war state of mind. As I got closer I clocked a few of them had guns. Their guns and numbers didn't faze me. I'd been here before, so many times. I walked up to them, ready to ride or die. "What do yous lot want?" I said aggressively.

"We want Darker." said a Fields boy. "He's been running up his mout' that he's the baddest in QB."

It was weak. It sounded so stupid and childish that it made me vex. So vex I was tempted to stab one of them. I couldn't believe that dem man had come round here for that. I took my knife out of its case but I also told them that this beef was getting boring and not even making any sense. Already Wildcat's brother had been killed by this foolishness, as had many other guys. And now they were coming 'ere with guns looking for my boy Darker, over what? Some proper foolishness. I could see Jadie and Wildcat were feeling what I was saying but one or two others didn't want to hear it.

Again, I begged them to put the beef to sleep and make some serious money. I felt like I had to speak my mind coz we weren't fourteen years old any more. But soon after I put my point across, Darker came running through the area on a mad one. "Who wants to kill me? Who wants to kill me?" he shouted. The Fields boys scattered thinking he had a gun. It was only a machete. When they realised they regrouped.

Darker realised they hadn't come to play games. For some reason no one tried to shoot me, even though I stood as a shield to protect him. It was a hectic situation. A tense stand-off. The Fields boys were moving around us on some hype ting, trying to get me out the way so they could get a clear shot at Darker. Somehow Risky-Talent managed to get Darker in a position where he was able to run.

Darker was lucky to get away but the other two boys he came with, Blacka and Likkle Vicious, were now surrounded with their backs against the wall. I pushed past the Fields boys as fast as I could to help. One of the top Fields boys went to stab Blacka. I pushed him away and told him to 'llow it. I was too late to save Likkle Vicious from getting stabbed in the leg, though. Chups! Then we saw the police approaching. We didn't wait for them to get close. Whoever had weapons threw them in some nearby bushes.

In my head, the bigger picture was becoming a little clearer. I wasn't me any more. When I looked in the mirror I didn't recognise the person I had become. I was always living next door to death, and thoughts of murdering Kane constantly haunted my mind. Deep down I knew I wasn't born a murderer. And even if I had killed Kane or any of his Fields boys, in my heart I wouldn't feel like I was a genuine murderer. Coz it has never been a part of my nature to want to kill anyone, even if they violated me. If I killed Kane I would have seen myself as someone who did it not coz I wanted to, but coz I felt I had to. I would have said that I was a person who killed coz my pride or ego got the better of me.

BACK TO THE CHASE

...It was easily a thirty-foot drop over the wall. Me and Darker jumped and fell fast and hard on Dalston train track. It was a madness the way man landed. I thought I broke my legs and buss my lip. We couldn't see jack. A foot wrong on one of them live rails and we wouldn't have to worry bout going to prison no more.

The plan was to breeze down the side of the track to the next station. But just before we got to the platform at Canonbury we got real paro. We saw what looked like torch lights flashing up ahead. We both froze. "Shit. Boi-dem's waiting for us at Canonbury." There was no time for no chit-chat.

The only way out was to climb the huge wall dividing the train track from the homes on the other side, so we did. Shit! The row of gardens we fell in was separated by even higher walls than the last one. That shit was disheartening. I was still wounded from the first jump. I crouched low for a breather. "Cuz, this is a long ting, dem feds need to just 'llow man."

We were laughing but it weren't even a joke ting, we was both bruck up. We had done alright to get this far, there was no way man was gonna give up now. 'Llow that. I ain't getting caught in someone's garden, like some bate crack head burglar. I ran up the next wall and barely caught the top with my fingertips and yanked myself up. Darker did his own spider man ting. Somehow we made it over.

Back on the streets, on Balls Pond Road somewhere, we styled it out like it was a minor. Behind the fronting we were blatantly happy to still have our freedom. We turned our coats inside out, put our hats in our pockets and bopped our way back to Dalston calmly, looking all boasy, like it was just another day in the manor. As we eased back into Hackney I remembered the 9mm rebore. "Bruv, times are hard right now. I'm not in no position to be dashing away a strap and shells."

We waited half an hour then went back to where I threw the gun. Darker kept an eye out for boi-dem as I searched. I found it on a patch of grass. I grinned. "Let's bounce. I got it fam." I tucked it in my waist, still paro that boi-dem might be watching. With that in mind, we bopped the back streets all the way to Stokey, to cool off at Denisha's.

Denisha was like a sister to me. She always looked out for my hungry belly and was one of the only girls I could trust. She passed me a plate of food which I appreciated a lot coz at this time of my life having a home cooked meal was rare. Rah, man's barely seventeen and it come like I'm trapped in this road ting. When did I start living like there's no tomorrow? Who the hell am I?

That night gave me a minute to look at things differently. I was frass out from my potent skunk spliff, but I now knew the answers to those two questions.

My past defined me. Pain, poverty, identity confusion and a bad temper all played a part. The real me stopped caring about tomorrow from time ago. Having seen the road life for what it was and hearing the hood stories from road man all around London, I realised most of us were trapped out 'ere. Mandem all over London were getting sucked into this mentality of reppin their endz. Which one of us ain't limited to which area we can go? Restricted in ways we can make money. Look at us; half of my bredrins were touring prisons up and down the country. We were carrying weapons like we had no other choice. But then we claimed that fear had nothing to do with it. If that's not a prisoner to the streets then, shit, I don't know what is.

Even though I had the sense to figure it all out I still bopped home from Stokey to Clarence with my gun in my waist. It's all good knowing you're in a trap, but it's another thing knowing how you're gonna get out of it. I couldn't see no way out. Every day I faced the possibility of doing life in a prison box, or being six feet under. I didn't let it faze me too much. By this age nuff people had told me I wouldn't live past my teenage years.

The next day, I went to Mare Street and bumped into my mum. I hadn't seen her since Nan's funeral. She looked stressed. I watched her for a minute then had to ask her why she looked so rough. "Mum, you're not smoking crack are you? Be real with me?"
"Son, don't be stupid. Things are just really hard right now," she laughed. It felt good to be wrong and stupid. It would have killed me to know she had turned to crack.

Later that night I was cotchin' with Darker, when he got a call from one of his people in Totty. Some madness going on and he wanted Darker to come and back the beef . Me being the street prisoner I was, picked up my gun and rolled with Darker to have his back.

When we got to Bruce Grove I was surprised to see that the brudder Darker wanted to back was a Totty boy called Ramone. He was with a boy called Cordell. Ramone wasn't my enemy but he definitely weren't my friend. He'd tried to get me buss up at school bare times, but Darker's my people and he's backing them, so I'm a back it. Me, Darker, Ramone and Cordell hailed each other with a spud. I took the gun off safety and bopped across the high road by the alleyway next to MacDees. When we got there my 'ride or die' changed, and I switched the ting back on safety.

It' s a small world innit? Ramone and Cordell had called Darker to help them war against man that I'm bless with. One of them, Millz, was a likkle brudder I looked out for when I was at D&K. He looked baffed to see me. We gave each other a spud. I could see by his body language that he didn't want me there. Something serious was about to pop off and he didn't want me to get caught in the crossfire.

I made sure Ramone and Cordell got back to the car safely. Me and Darker left the scene and drove back to Hackney. The issue between

Ramone, Cordell and the other Totty boys weren't put to rest. They
would have to sort that shit out another day, without my presence.

SIX MONTHS OF MADNESS

AUGUST 2002 - JANUARY 2003

Even with my little rep and strap I still wasn't at peace in Pembury. I can't even lie, I got so caught up in my own hype I started to believe it. It was crazy. Gyal on road who I took a liking to and tried to get acquainted with had already heard about me. Before I'd even get to finish asking a girl her name, she would tell me who I am.

I went to bed every night with a gun under my pillow. I wasn't scared of any specific crew or person, but I did cared about losing my life to the streets whenever I thought about it too deeply.

Early one Saturday morning a knock on the door woke me. I looked through the peephole to see two Jehova's Witnesses standing there. I let them in coz the last time they came I promised I would give them five minutes of my time. As they entered, I lit the end of a bed-time spliff from the night before. They kept asking me if my parents were around. I just ignored them. Then one of them asked, "Is that a gun under your pillow?" I nodded. I was mad that they saw it coz I thought it was well hidden. I asked them to leave. I was done with all that holy talk.

--

I had just got the keys to my new flat. Finally, the days of living in a stinking hostel, sharing nasty kitchens and bathrooms, were over. I didn't move far. Still in Pembury, just round the corner from Hackney

Downs Park on Cricketfield Road.

One evening, Me and Darker were chilling at my yard. He said he wanted to link up with Rizla and Cordell. I agreed to roll coz I wanted to get out of the endz for a bit. At this point Darker was one of the only people I really rolled with. We jumped into his car and drove to Cordell's.

We were jammin at Cordell's yard in Edmonton when dem man decided they wanted to get a munch on Tottenham High Road from Too Sweet. One of Rizla's youngers wanted to hang with us, so him and his friends followed us to the take away in their car. Young Buck was a lost younger with something to prove and a blind sense of loyalty. Just like me, he got stabbed at fourteen, and it clearly affected his thinking. He was reckless. Rizla and Cordell had this yute gassed up differently, boasting that he was a young don in the making. He was always on the beef. When I looked in his eyes, it was like looking into a mirror.

On the way to Too Sweet in N15, we drove through Tottenham High Road and saw nuff people coming out of a rave. Darker and the others wanted to stop and cherps some gyal. Usually I would have been the first to drop the girls dem one-liners, but that night I wasn't feeling it. I just wanted to go get a munch from Too Sweet and then go to my yard. I didn't feel comfortable chilling in Tottenham any more. I didn't know where I stood with them. I was sick and tired of Tottenham man making out that every single Hackney boy was to blame for Popcorn's death. For years I tried to keep my Totty friendships yet most of the time I was made to feel uncomfortable and unwelcome when I went to chill in my original endz. But Darker, Young Buck and the other man saw some gyals and got excited so we parked up.

We sat in the car and eventually clocked a Hackney man. It was Geezer's older brother who gave me strict orders to come out the endz now because there was nuff older Tottenham boys in the dance. Then he took his own advice and left. Everyone I was with except for Darker was from Tottenham, so none of them had a problem getting out of their car and mingling. Although Darker was from Hackney, his face wasn't bate in Tottenham so when he saw a group of lighties that he wanted to cherpse, he just got out of the car to chat to them.

I was a well known guy from Hackney and so was my brother, so I decided to be smart and stay in the car. I didn't want any trouble that day. With the seat reclined and my hat pulled down over my face, I was daydreaming about my Nan when I heard some girls arguing. This made me look in the rear view mirror and I clocked a group of guys surrounding Darker. The second I see my boy in trouble, I jumped out the car and breezed towards the madness to back him.

Young Buck must have had the same frame of mind because he came charging in to try and save Darker. None of us were sure what was about to go down. The next thing I know, there's blood everywhere and everyone began to scatter. At that point I didn't know whose blood it was but one someone got stabbed.

OCTOBER

I was at home relaxing when I got a phone call from Darker to come check him coz it was his birthday. He was gonna celebrate at Palace Pavilion which was just around the corner from my new flat. I got dressed - put my gold chain on - and then met up with two of my boys, Ace of Spades and Yellowman. We made our way on foot to Lower Clapton but as we got closer, we noticed people were standing by watching a group of about twenty guys rushing one boy. I soon clocked that it wasn't anyone from Hackney. It was a click I didn't even know. This was really strange, coz only Hackney boys would terrorise the streets of the borough in the way these boys were.

Passers-by looked terrified. I was just confused as to where all the Hackney boys were. "This is dodgy. Fuck that, I'm going to get my ting," I said to Ace of Spades and Yellowman.

As we walked back the crew started following us. They had knives and bottles . Coz it was my endz my ego wasn't about to let these boys come terrorise me. I stopped and faced them. "You man don't want it with me," I said, then turned and carried on. They were still following us, though, and getting closer. I could have run but, as usual, my bad temper got the better of me. I turned and punched the biggest boy in the face. Then the next, and it was on.

Before I could land another punch, I felt the harsh sting of CS gas as someone snatched at my chain. The pepper spray affected my vision so I grabbed the nearest boy in an arm lock and used him as a punchbag. But I was getting jumped and stabbed in the back. I fell to the ground, still holding on to the boy, still fighting back. I heard some girls across the road screaming my name. That didn't stop me fighting. Then one of the boys shouted, "He's crazy. Just shoot him, man. Shoot him and done."

One of them stood over me and fired a shot. I felt blood pouring down my head, my face and my neck. But it wasn't from the gunshot, the boy missed his mark. The boy I was holding managed to get free and backed off with the others. My eyes were stinging from the gas, I couldn't see shit. Ace of Spades, Yellowman and a Jamaican man who was passing, pulled me up to run. Fuck all that running, these pricks better kill me. From a distance of about fifteen feet the boys started shooting off the ting at me and Ace. Bare gunshot was flying around. Somehow Ace and the Jamaican managed to drag me away to safety.

The boys were at the top of my road now so we couldn't even get back to my flat. We ended up in the opposite direction by my old hostel. I was losing a lot of blood so I decided to stop there. I rang the bell of my ex-neighbour and good friend Gina. She was shocked to see me covered in blood. That's when I realised I had been stabbed in the head.

Gina took me in and helped me clean the blood off and wash the pepper spray from my eyes. Then I breezed back to my flat, got my gun and ran as fast as I could back to Palace Pavilion to find the boys who did this. Blood was still pouring down my head. It wouldn't stop. Back outside Palace P I asked anyone and everyone, "Where did dem boys go?"

Nobody seemed to know.

I saw Jadie and Neds from Fields outside the dance. Jadie stopped to see if I was okay. He was pissed off to see me covered in blood but he made it a thing to stand by me as I went looking to duppy the yutes. It was unreal. Here I was, ready to roll on whoever nearly took my life, and I only had a Fields boy by my side. Jadie kept telling me to go to the hospital coz there was nuff blood pouring from the stab in my head. But I'm a stubborn one.

Out of nowhere, my brother turned up ready to roll. I was too angry to talk to him. I wanted to do things my way. I didn't want to listen to my brother, Jadie or anyone. I just wanted to lick someone down and nobody seemed to know who they were.

Someone mentioned that there was another under 21s rave at Oceans in Mare Street, fifteen minutes walk away. I had a feeling that the boys, whoever they were, might have gone there. To get Jadie off my case I told him I was going to hospital, but instead I went to Oceans. I confronted a few groups of boys that I didn't know, but none of them were the boys I was looking for. Blood was still pouring like crazy and I began to feel dizzy. I got frustrated. These boys seemed to have vanished out of Hackney.

I eventually made my way to Homerton Hospital. When I got to A&E, the receptionist looked at me and asked, "What did you get stabbed with?"

I swore. "Why do you guys always ask me silly questions when I get stabbed?"

"Calm down, sir, or you'll have to leave," she said.

I couldn't calm down. I left in a rage and went home to sleep, my head still bleeding, my gun under the pillow. It was covered in blood when I woke the next morning. I charged up my phone to see over seventy missed calls. I started phoning back. People were saying that they heard I was dead. There were rumours that I had been shot in the head.

The crazy thing is that I was more vex that they took my chain than the fact that they nearly took my life. I don't know what it was, I can't really explain it, but when I had my blinging chain around my neck it made me feel like I was the man. Plus it was the fact that I had worked hard for it.

I phoned back Darker to ask him where the hell he was the night before. He started telling me some crazy story that the Fields boys were shooting at him minutes before I got there. I wasn't fully convinced by that story, but I didn't really wanna challenge what he was saying. I didn't wanna risk our friendship. I barely had any friends left and I hated being alone. But the more I thought about it, the more I got mad with confusion. Coz Darker was the one who called me in the first place and told me to meet him at Palace P for his birthday.

Why didn't he phone man to warn me not to go there? If the Fields boys were shooting at him I'd be a target as well. Why didn't he phone me?

My anger died down. In my heart I believed that my boy Darker would never purposely do anything to put my life at risk. Me and Darker linked up later that evening to chat face to face about the madness the night before. To my surprise, Darker told me he heard that some of the Holly Street boys were happy to hear that we got fucked up. I couldn't believe that the same boys man used to ride or die for were happy to hear I nearly got killed. By now I was hurting about so many things and just didn't want to hurt no more. More than anything doh, I was fed up of feeling betrayed and like no one cared about my life.

We decided to go to Holly Street to address those who were talking bad mind. We wanted to get every person who we felt wanted to see our downfall or wanted us dead. We made a list of all da mandem we planned to hurt that night. Our 'kill bill' list. First on the list for chatting shit was Marcus. When we got to Holly Street, Marcus, Risky-Talent, and some other boy were chilling there. Darker broke a bottle and moved to Marcus straight away - no long ting. He grabbed him by the throat and started to jook him up with the broken glass. "It wasn't me, it was Birdman," Marcus pleaded.

We went looking for Birdman. Even though me and Birdman were cool before, the second I heard that rumour of him being happy that I nearly died, all forms of friendship went out the window. We made our way to Geezer's house and I told someone to go inside and tell

Birdman to meet me round the corner. When Birdman came to meet me I looked at him and said, "What's this I'm hearing you're saying, cuz? You're happy to hear I got stabbed in the head, yeah? You think I think I'm too bad, yeah?"

I was so angry. I didn't even wait to hear his side of the story. The way I moved to him was sick. Darker tried to get involved but I pushed him off coz I wanted a fair one-on-one. Some other Holly Street boys watched but didn't get involved.

After I handled business with Birdman, me and Darker went to find the others on the 'kill bill' list. We went to Fields, then Totty, but we didn't find no one. So we just went home.

Years later I had to man up and give Birdman an apology. I'd realised that Darker wasn't who I thought he was. He was just manipulating my emotions for his own ends. But at the time, he was the only one I felt I could trust so I never questioned his motives.

--

NOVEMBER

I was settling in and moving things around in my new flat. My phone rang. It was a number I didn't recognise. When I answered it the person said, "Robyn Travis? This is DC Reeves. You're wanted for murder." I laughed and hung up. It sounded like a prank call from one of da mandem. He kept phoning back. I kept blanking the calls. After a while it was getting on my nerves so I decided to answer.

"We have a warrant for your arrest," the man said. "As of now, Mr Travis, you are on the run." I phoned Darker to find out if it was him running joke but I couldn't get through. Next day I got a call from a 01 sutt'n number. I answered and it was Darker. "Wah gwarn?" I said. "You didn't prank call man yesterday, did you?"

"Nah, bruv, I don't have my blower. I just got locked up, I'm phoning you from jail fam."

Darker told me he was inside for armed robbery. I was totally pissed for him. Chups.

The next day I called my solicitor and asked him to phone boi-dem about the calls. He called back an hour later and confirmed the fuckery. I was officially on the run, but for attempted murder.

My solicitor told me to meet him the next day at Tottenham police station. He advised me to bring my toothbrush as I was likely to be sent to prison on remand until the court case. I found out that the charge was to do with the beef on Tottenham High Road the time I was with Darker and Young Buck and we got caught up in a madness on the way to get a munch from Too Sweet. At the station my solicitor took me to one side before we went in for questioning.

"I have to tell you, Rob, it's not looking good. I can almost guarantee that you'll be denied any form of bail. You know the procedure, you'll be held in custody overnight and put on remand until the trial."

"Cool."

"One more thing, Rob, don't let this detective make you lose your temper in there. This DC Reeves guy looks like he wants to lock you up and throw away the key. Keep your cool."

"Cool, Mr Smith. I got this."

In the interview room the DC was smiling. "Good thing you turned yourself in son, the gang was getting fed up of looking for ya," he said.

Who's this cuntstable calling 'son'? Prick. He was just trying to get a reaction. I ignored him and sat down quietly for the interview. This is some joke ting. I've been shift so many times growing up that I knew exactly what he was gonna say before he said it. But for the purpose of the tape he read my rights anyway. I had to shake my head. I swear it ain't normal to know man's rights word for word.
Growing up man never rated the feds. Most of them pigs were cold to mandem. Feds had me paro, period. Whenever I was innocent of a crime they still made me feel guilty. So my mind was programmed to

always expect the worst possible outcome.

The DC went straight into it. He threw some garments covered in blood on the table.

"Mr Travis, we got a bunch of witnesses that say you tried to kill Kaiya Truman. What do you say?"

"No Comment."

"All right, let's forget the games, Mr Travis. Do you know a young man named Darren?

"No comment."

"Well, he said that you attacked and chased after him and his friends and tried to kill them. Darren seems to knows you very well. Darren says he went to City and Islington College with you. Darren knows you so well that he easily picked you out on our video line up. He says you had quite a rep in college."

"No comment." Who the fuck is Darren? I know about fifteen Darrens.

I was gonna say 'no comment' all day, but then I thought, nah, forget all that. Let me say it how I saw it. "It was self defence. No one likes us Hackney boys. All I remember is I was outnumbered by nuff of them. It was them against me. I had to run to get home in one piece."

After I explained my version of events in detail, the DC said, "I know you don't expect us to believe that's what really happened, Mr Travis?"

"Believe what you want."

He went red in the face then said, "Look, we know you're holding back, we know you didn't start this. Do yourself a favour and save yourself a longer sentence by telling us who your mate is. The victim, Kaiya, described him as a dark skinned guy with a gold tooth.

I smiled with my gold tooth showing. "Everyone's got a gold tooth these days."

"Look, mate, STOP trying to be a loyal friend. Darren and Kaiya both said in their statements that you weren't there when it started. It started with your mate, you know, the one, the dark skinned guy with the gold tooth. So just tell us who he is, and we'll get ya a lighter sentence."

"Sorry, I don't know who you're on about, guvna."

The detective looked vex, like he wanted to punch my jaw off. The interview went on for ages. He kept going on about my mate with the dark skin and the gold tooth, and I just went back into my 'no comment' behaviour. Talk done. The interview was terminated when he realised I wouldn't snitch. I was placed in a cell and later called to the desk and told that I was being released with bail conditions until the date of the trial.

Everyone, even me, was surprised I got bail. Freedom's a good reason to smile but I was still angry that these boys had the cheek to go to police and snitch, when it was them who started the beef. Everyone knows the rules of the streets. If you're on the beef you don't go to police. You just don't do it.

My solicitor dropped me off near my house. "Robyn," he said, "I have never met a client like you in all my years as a solicitor. I have watched you grow up and it seems that you're always in a situation. You're always being locked up or in court. In my eyes, you're really not such a bad kid. Even if you don't recognise it yet, I think you're a decent lad." I was confused that my solicitor was calling me a decent person, considering he had just got me out on bail on an attempted murder charge. He believed me but could tell I was willing to serve time for what happened to Kaiya Truman.

He didn't have to, but he dropped me home in his brand new sports car. Most man on road didn't trust their solicitors, but I knew mine had my back to the end from time. I also knew how lucky I was to be back on road.

DECEMBER

The Hackney/Tottenham beef added another brother, Buckhead, to the death count. I knew that this murder would cause the tension between Hackney and Tottenham to grow. Popcorn's murder in '97 had kept the tit-for-tat killings rolling for years. The loss of Buckhead was guaranteed to take the beef to a new level. No doubt.

--

JANUARY

Some weeks later, I asked my boy D-Lowe to roll with me to a rave in Green Lanes. I was dijjy about being in Totty and wasn't sure we would pass the door search coz I had my gun on me. But I managed to slip it in. Since that shootout, I had to make sure I was ready to buss the ting. You can't be a part-time bad man out 'ere. I walked through the rave nodding to a few people I knew, but I didn't stop to talk to them. The Tottenham, Wood Green and Edmonton boys were chilling in their separate groups. I saw Ramone and then my boy Od'z from Tiverton, but I didn't want to blend with his boys so stayed low with D-Lowe.

Meanwhile some older Totty boys walked in the rave - mandem who my brother fought on the bus years earlier. They came and stood to the left of me. A few of them gave Ramone a spud. They were about to touch fists with me but paused when they clocked my grill. I kept my hands on my gun, in case. One of them leaned forward and spoke into Ramone's ear. Then they walked off into the crowd but appeared to be making bare funny movements.

Od'z was standing behind me with his Tiverton crew. He looked worried. "Robyn, real talk, I think you should leave y'know. I think they're gonna move to you," he said. I ignored him at first but then I saw Ramone move away and stand by the entrance. I was thinking maybe they told him to keep a lookout, just in case I tried to escape. I couldn't believe it. It looked like Ramone was a part of a plan to get me seriously hurt. If that was the case, it was fuckery. Talk about badmind. It was only a few months earlier that I was prepared to back him.

I let D-Lowe know about the movements and said we needed to slip out ASAP. It was only then that he clocked our predicament. "Robyn, y'know man are the only Hackney boys in 'ere," he said. We headed towards the exit.

When we got to the door I gave Ramone one dirty look. Then I felt a hand on my shoulder. It was Bianca, an old friend. "I ain't seen you in time," she said. "And I was speaking 'bout you today. You're gonna live long." I was nervous about the 'kill or be killed' situation, but Bianca's words gave me a sense of peace. I told her to phone me, then me and D-Lowe ducked out.

Outside I was mad as hell. I saw Hugo Boss, a boy I knew from Hackney. I asked him what he was doing in Totty by himself like he was a T town boy. I switched on him and called him a snake. I was just about to gun butt him when D-Lowe said, "Trav, it's long, 'llow him. We ain't got time for that. Let's get out of here. NOW."

We went to D-Lowe's house, where I laid my head to rest for the night, thinking I could have met my maker tonight. I was a Hackney boy whose brother had beef with dem North man. I would have been the ideal target. They were still mourning Buckhead. Maybe I was a hypocrite for calling Hugo a snake for acting casual In T. He weren't no different from me, just a Hackney boy in a Totty boy rave. I couldn't trust no one out 'ere. Again.

Why couldn't I go anywhere in Hackney or Tottenham - the two places I grew up - without taking my gun? I couldn't sleep properly. I kept having the same nightmare. I was getting shot over and over again by guys I was once friends with. All I could hear were voices saying, "I told you you're not gonna live to see 18."

TIME TO LAY LOW

Talk about being broke. At times it felt like my stomach was touching my back. Ah well, it is what it is. I swore that I would never work in a shit cleaning job again, but if I wanted to go legit my only option was to clean for a living, coz that's the only thing I had on my CV. Every other job I went for wouldn't hire me coz I had more convictions than qualifications.

Fuck a nine to five then. I'm not on that shit no more. But I needed some of that queen's head. Thank God I'm getting benefits to pay the rent. If it wasn't for that I would be out 'ere with certain other man jumping counters.

At times I felt I had the right to rob and steal. Then I'd remember dem one-liners Nan used to say. Like, 'If you don't need something don't kill up yourself to get it', 'Easy come easy go'. And the one I hated the most, coz I had the hardest of ears was, 'Who don't hear, must feel'.

What choice have I got? I need to stack some peas. Most of my Job Centre money went on electric, gas and rent. The rest was divided on food and weed.

The temptation to be a top shotta was stronger than ever. I had to fight it. It wasn't about chasing dreams it was just about surviving. Eff it, lemme stay broke and lay low.

My attitude wasn't built for the drugs game. I could have stolen bare man's cats. That attitude wouldn't have got me nowhere doh, except more hype and beef. I really didn't need that. I knew the drug game as well as the next road man, but I had already seen the good and the bad side of that life. Under my mum's roof. My brother was a dream chaser, mum's husband was the top feen, my heart just weren't in it. I couldn't add to the game that tore my family apart.

Things had changed on the road as well; it was clear that the bad bwoy percentage was increasing. Random new guys were trying to rep the endz like it was fashion. It's like everyone wanted to be the King of Hackney. Since when did everybody turn badman?

I don't know the answer, but I know that the film *Paid in Full* and 50 Cent's album *Get Rich Or Die Tryin'* had just come out. From where I was standing it felt like man who weren't sayin nothing back in the day on road, thought they were veterans. It was some joke ting. It's like every man on road decided to be gangsta. New-time bad boys and drug dealers were coming out of nowhere. Youngers wanted to be just like us but even badder. One or two youngers on various blocks were getting ahead of themselves. With their little drugs money and a burner tucked in their waist, no one couldn't tell them nothing no more. Half of these guys didn't know about the road life but were looking for hood ratings. Certain man were even wearing bullet proof vests and durags. They'd never even been stabbed or shot but everyone who couldn't fight had guns and really believed they were the bad boys now. I had a good excuse to have a vest; I felt like my time to die was coming and I would be crazy for not wearing one. When I prayed that feeling went away but things were changing out 'ere. It was best for me to just lay low until this attempted M charge was off my head. Then I could be free.

On June 9th 2003, Woodz and his girl, Chloe, came my flat to chill. I met Woodz back in the day and we became closer bredrins as time went on. We were smoking weed when my phone rang. It was Mammal one of the older Pembury boys. He sounded worried and asked me if I was OK.

"Yeah, why?"

"Bruv, if you're outside come off road NOW. Dem Tottenham boys are in the hood shooting after Hackney man. Be careful."

"Shooting after who?"

" I dunno, Rob, just stay off road."

"Aite cool, good looking out, fam." I hung up.

Mammal was chatting like he was ready to rep the block or sutt'n. North man killed his brother back in the day so he had a valid reason to be vex that they were bussin shots in the hood. I didn't know whether to take what Mammal was saying as gospel but summertime in the hood there's always a drama so I couldn't take the chat too lightly. Strange, doh. It's broad daylight. Why would Totty man roll on us so bate in the day? I had ratings for Mammal as an older looking out for man, so I took his advice and stayed put.

Chloe went to use the bathroom. Moments later she came breezing out with one hand on her phone and the other on her head, standing there in shock. "Oh my God. Where? When?" She turned to me and Woodz. "Jadie's just been shot. In Fields." Jadie was Chloe's ex. She screamed and ran out. Woodz went after her. I got my gun and followed.

Minutes later we were in London Fields Park. It was mayhem. The ambulance was just taking Jadie away. His blood was everywhere. It looked like boi dem weren't taking it seriously and a riot was about to kick off between them and the Fields boys. I heard the ambulance took half an hour to arrive.

"Rob, they shot Jadie," someone shouted. It was Jadie's boy, Nedz. He bopped up and hugged me in front of everyone. He couldn't even catch his breath to chat properly whilst crying for his boy. "Rob, they shot J, they shot J," he carried on.

As he hugged me I got a chill down my spine and that nervous gut feeling. I remembered Mammal's call earlier. I put two and two together and clocked that it must have been a Tottenham boy who shot

Jadie. I went on a mad one on the spot and wanted to go to North to handle my business. They can't shoot J like that. Are they fucking mad?

All of a sudden Not-Nice started acting in a way. He pulled Nedz away from me. I was baffled. The way he had done it you would have thought I was the enemy or sutt'n. I was mad at Not-Nice for that. He knew that me and Jadie were boys. He didn't need to go on like that. But I kept my calm and gave him a dirty look back. I didn't care who felt a way towards me. Man must be crazy if they think I came here to beg friend. Fuck what peeps think, Jadie had my back when I got stabbed in the head. I owe him one.

"Who done it?" I shouted, my hand on my strap. I wanted to know now so I could roll on the exact same boy who pulled the trigger. I wanted to lick it down. As I was wildin out one of the older Fields boys, Phatz, bopped up to me and quietly said, "Rob, it was your Holly Street boys that done it." I froze. It didn't make no sense.

Could they really be responsible for shooting the one boy from Fields that I'm bless with? What the fuck did they shoot him for? As far as I know, he ain't even involved in the beef like that. Me and J were growing out of this postcode bullshit, trying to look past that. I looked around. Nuff people were crying and screaming. Then I clocked the pattern. Not-Nice's moves started to make sense. Couple Fields man were looking at me like I was public enemy number one. I couldn't even front like I didn't have mad beef with certain man surrounding me before this day. But most of us on the scene were fully aware that I weren't down for my Holly Street boys like I used to be. The whole hood knew I stabbed Marcus on my Nan's doorstep just a year earlier. Even certain man from North knew that. None of that shit seemed to matter though. In everyone's eyes I was one of the enemy.

Robyn Travis = Holly Street - and that's that.

If these man even think about moving to me, it's gonna be a shootout in front of the cops. Fuck that, I ain't 'aving it! I looked at the police, and couldn't believe what I saw. A lot of them were smiling like they was doing a shift at Carnival. It made me sick to my stomach. I put my hands to my head then the penny dropped.

The same spot where Jadie got shot was the same rarse place where this Holly Street and Fields beef started years earlier. We cut out; I went home to Pembury and prayed for Jadie. My world was on pause. Deep down I didn't believe God had the power to make a brother survive that shooting. As I was waiting to hear the latest my phone rang. "He's gone, blud. Jadie's dead," the caller said. God weren't hearing or listening. It felt like he had washed his hands of all da mandem from H and T town. I called my brother about what happened and he said he heard the fuckery already.

I'm not sure if I blinked the whole night. Sleep was the last thing on my mind. I heard the birds whistling. The sun was rising but I was still sitting there, phone in hand. Shock wasn't the word. Jadie's dead, why the fuck didn't I stop this. Why J?

I saw Death coming from long-time, but I didn't think that it was coming for such a cool brother like J. I thought death would be looking for the most hated boys from E8, either side of Queensbridge. I can't even lie, I was totally baffed. Who thought they had a good enough reason to kill him? Apart from me, Geezer and Marcus, none of da mandem ever had it out with the Fields boys. So what pushed a man to do this? Real talk, lemme not pass any judgement. God knows I ain't perfect but Jadie's death was ripping the heart out of Hackney.

I didn't have no one to talk to about it so I bottled up my feelings, alone out 'ere with a bag of weed and my thoughts. One of my closest friends, Janet, from Tottenham came to see me. She said it looked like I was fighting to hold back my temper and tears. Me cry? Nah never that. Only time I couldn't fight the tears was when Nan died. Fuck shedding a tear now. I can't let no one see my pain.

I kept daydreaming about how them bullets ripped through a brother and left a hole in his stomach. I tried to imagine the pain. I had this picture in my head of his mum on her knees, screaming "Why Lord, why?" and tears being shed by the brother's family, and everyone else who loved him.

The following day I heard talk of who was supposed to be involved and how it happened. I got an insight but things weren't much clearer. Talk on road was that Holly Street boys didn't roll alone. The streets were chatting like couple Square boys were involved. I knew most of the Square boys who were said to be involved coz 'nuff of the Square lot were bless with man. When I heard Top-Shotta's name mentioned it made it worse, coz I got mad love for him. I was more confused to hear the streets chat like Mintz, Reckless and Marcus from Holly Street were to blame.

These guys weren't no Holly Street soldiers, they weren't on this bad bwoy ting when Fields came round the endz for us back then. Where was that bad bwoy attitude when I got stabbed? These same man accused for J's killing ran and left me for dead. But then, everyone had a gun now, so everyone's a gangsta. Call me strange and that but I'm finding it hard to rate certain man involved.

The street talk didn't bring me peace of mind. Apart from Mintz and Top-Shotta, I couldn't care about those who were rumoured to be involved. I had stabbed Marcus a year earlier and 'round that same time I almost got into a fight with Reckless. We both had shanks on us. Reckless had just come out of prison for stabbing someone. God knows how we didn't shank each other up.

I knew Marcus and Reckless secretly had it out for me. Most of these man were couple years older than me. They didn't care about the times I had their back on road, things were different now.
If it's true Mintz was involved, I did hear that Fields boys rushed him and took his chain a year before.

I thought that beef was dead, doh, coz Mintz's older brother grew up with dem Fields man. I thought they squashed that shit. I remember Top-Shotta telling me the same madness - Fields boys rushed him and took his chain. But I can't remember him mentioning Jadie's name. This shit's a lot right now.

As angry as I was about Jadie's death, I couldn't be no hypocrite. Knowing me, I would have reacted in the same way if a man tried to take my tings. Not saying the chat on road was gospel but, if it was, did any man on road really have the right to feel a way?

When it came to backing beef we could all be hypocrites. Especially me. I was backing man left, right and centre; no questions asked and knowing they were in the wrong. I weren't in no position to be judging anyone.

Let's be real, I'm on bail for attempted murder and know exactly how it feels when a group of boys take your chain and your life for granted. That shit ain't nice. It can make a good guy turn wicked. No one on road wants to hear any "squash the beef" talk after getting robbed or stabbed.

I had no idea that the death of a Fields boy would affect me so much. I can't even say it like that. Jadie weren't just any Fields boy, he was a true friend. He weren't no badmind yute. I always saw the good in him. I always saw the good in Mintz and Top Shotta too. I just hoped the rumours weren't true. We all know the streets can re-mix shit.

MY PREDICAMENT

A few days had passed since the murder. Out of nowhere I started getting bare death threats. People were phoning day and night saying, "Robyn, you're dead. You think you're a bad man, yeah? You're dead." Whoever made the calls didn't do it alone. There was 'nuff dudes in the background talking that greaze. I assumed it was the Fields boys, but I wasn't 100%.

I couldn't stand the fool-fool death threats. These dudes were drawing me out. I just felt to come out and get it poppin. Then I switched. "I didn't kill Jadie, so stop chatting shit. If you wanna kill me, come and do your ting." I was still a one man army at a time of an E8 war. I had to watch my back.

Some girls I knew phoned and told me that they heard it was me who killed Jadie, and wanted to know if it was true. I got mad when I heard that rumour. What type of fuckery ...? I heard some next rumours that Holly Street boys were chatting my name and 'traitor' in the same sentence. All coz I was angry Jadie got killed. I didn't even take that chat serious. How can I be a traitor? Forget dem pricks. Make a man call me a traitor to my face and see what happens. Chups! Where I come from we don't have it from no one. I got ready to kill anyone who tried it.

If I go out I'm going out bussing my ting. Not coz I wanted to kill but coz I'm just not having it. And I really don't have time to watch my back. Fear was trying to creep its way back into my life, I weren't having a bar of it. So I got my cotton buds and made sure my gun was oiled and ready.

A few weeks after the madness I went to E5 to pay my mum an over-due visit. I hadn't seen her since we started chatting again. But after J died I decided that life was too short to hold feelings, so I made the effort. I also wanted her to meet the new girl in my life. I couldn't just bring any old gyal on road to mum's yard. Mum didn't trust most girls I liked. But I weren't watching that, I knew this one was a keeper. The girl I'm on about just so happened to be my friend Janet from Tottenham. It didn't matter that she was from Totty, she was good people. I rated her highly coz she passed all dem 21 questions that 50 Cent was rapping about. The last thing a brother needs is a hype chick. But I didn't even need to question it. Mum took a liking to her straight away so it was a good look.

Me and mum went in the kitchen and I told her the sad news of Jadie's death. She didn't even say a word, she just outed her cigarette and dropped a few tears. I was kinda shocked still. She always taught me not to cry over nothing and there she was standing in the kitchen in tears. I weren't good at doing all that hugging/ don't cry/'I love you mum' stuff. So I just said, "Why are you crying for? That's not like you."

"Every time another young black boy is killed, it breaks my heart like it was my own son. You lot need to stop this foolishness. What are you killing off each other for?"

Real talk. I couldn't hear that. I didn't know why. What type of ques-tion's that? All I know is, certain man are chatting like they want me dead. "What can I say, mum, it is what it is. Life, innit?"

"That don't sound like life to me, son."

We left my mum's and headed towards Homerton train station when we bumped into a Fields boy jammin' in the passenger seat of some black car. He was cool, though; we were good friends in Lon-don Fields primary. He looked out the tinted window. "Wah gwarn, Robs?" he smiled. I nodded and that was it, no long chat, we both just kept it moving.

Me and Jan carried on. At the station we walked up the stairs to the platform, which overlooked the street below. Whilst we were waiting for the train we saw the same car Benny was in, slowly driving past. One of the other passengers looked up and clocked me. The car came to a stop near the end of Berger Road just before Digby. From where we were standing on the platform, me and Jan could still see them parked up with the engine running. Is it beef right now? They were moving funny, like they were getting ready for a drive-by or sutt'n.

My brain didn't have no time to register what dem man was up to. All I heard was the wheel spin and the car breezing towards us. I stepped to my left and blocked Jan, coz it looked like these man were getting ready to buss shots. I quickly cocked back the ting and got ready to buss it in return. I saw dem man looking up as the car got closer to where we were standing. Usually, I'm the hot-headed type to act first, ask questions later, but sutt'n told me not to shoot. They drove past, slowly, giving me face.

"Jan, did you just see the fuckery? Y'know that was the same brudder that said, 'Wah gwarn' to me down the road. And now ten minutes later man are moving like they wanna shoot me. Am I going mad out 'ere? Jan, did that shit really just happen?"

My girl couldn't even chat. She just held my arm and shook her head in disbelief. I had a feeling that this shit was becoming as real to her as it was to me. I was baffled. Like I said, I thought me and that yute was bless. We never had a problem. I couldn't make sense of why they were parked up outside the station because they were heading towards Cassland in the opposite direction. Cassland Road is a one way. Wick Road is a one way too.

So why the fuck would dem man drive round in a big circle, just to park outside a train station where I happened to be standing? My fingers were getting itchy. Rarse! Dem Fields boys weren't ramping when they private numbered me saying they're gonna lick me down. I felt tempted to go get a BIG ting, jump on the back of a superbike and go light the place up.

Actions speak louder than words. I couldn't allow myself to get too emotional. Too many people were acting off emotions out here on the roads. The reality was I didn't see them with a gun. All I knew was that the car was moving dodgy. I wasn't looking to go to jail for something I wasn't sure about.

Real talk, doh, was a man really gonna shoot me in front of my girl? Later that night I asked my girl how she felt about that little madness earlier. "Honestly Robyn," she said, "I was more scared at what you were going to do. When I saw you grab your gun, I thought it was over."

IF I RUN I'M SCARED, IF I STAY I'M DEAD

I needed to get outta Hackney. It was getting way too warm for me out 'ere. It come like half of Hackney wanted me dead. And I was still on bail for this brudder from Totty. What a life.

The heat was on. So I made a phone call to my Uncle in Northampton and he told me to come and stay till the heat cools down. Family issues still surrounded us, but Unc came through.

A week later I went to see my social worker. "Things are getting a bit crazy out here. Right now, I'm on bail for one attempted murder charge. And one brother I know has just been killed by a next brudder. Long story short. I need a transfer out of Hackney, like now. If I don't leave real soon, I'm either gonna get lifed off in prison or end up dead."

My social worker could see what time it was. He wanted to do whatever he could to stop me from killing or being killed. He contacted his manager on the spot and within weeks I was offered a flat. "Where the hell is Wolverhampton?"

I was thinking somewhere nearer home still, but that was my only option. I told the social worker to forget it. He was one of them old skool African men who didn't sweet-talk. He just said, "Look, nephew, a man with too much pride is a foolish man." Chups! I'm not leaving my hometown. Nah, fuck that. But, after thinking about it for a while I decided to put down this pride business. It's what made me a prisoner to the streets in the first place. I stuck with my first instinct and went ghost. Clean out of Hackney and Totty.

Getting away was the best thing. I soon adapted to the quiet life. Mum gave me money from my Nan's will to buy a car to get about. All I had to do now was find out where the local weed sellers were. Once I did, I smoked all day. There was nothing else to do on bail. I couldn't go to college or look a job coz there was a good chance I was going to jail. And I had no plans to return to London, except for my court case in October. In Wolverhampton I decided to go to church to look for God. I couldn't find him, but I met a lady called Jackie. She was good people. She regularly called to check on me and invite me to the service. Her invitations were in vain. I just wasn't feeling it. She said she would ask the church to pray for me about my court case. I rated her highly for that. If I was found guilty I would need their prayers.

Apart from Jackie and a few Hackney goons who were up there, I hardly spoke to anyone. Every so often my girl, Jan, would come from London to see me. My mum called every now and then, she knew I was a city boy at heart, I weren't used to living in the sticks. Every time she called she begged me to come to London to visit. I couldn't tell her that London was like a death trap for me. So I promised I would come soon.

A month went by before I decided to drive down to see my girl in Totty and my mum in Hackney. As I exited the M1 for London my whole spirit felt uneasy. I had only reached Holloway Road in North London when I saw my old Holly Street friend Pablo. He used to be like a brother to me but he was a Fields boy now so I didn't know where we stood. He was behind me with his friend Escobar. I beeped and told them to pull over. I jumped out of my car and bopped up to them.

"Who's saying what now? Who was giving me the death threats down the phone 'bout killing me?" I had my hammer ready to use.

"Nah, Rob, no one ain't chattin your name," they said. "Everyone knows who did it now."

I calmed down a little and told them to tell their Fields boys, "If anyone wants to move to me, then cool. I'm still on this ting. But don't make out it's over Jadie. Everyone knows that me and J were cool."

I got back in my car and drove to Hackney to see my mum. I left my gun there coz I was on bail and couldn't risk getting caught by boidem. Then I drove to my girl's. That's where I spent most of my time. Crazy, I felt safer in Tottenham than I did in Hackney, at that point.

I had only come for a week. Three days before it was time to go back to Wolverhampton, I was jammin at my mum's flat in Homerton when my phone rang. It was my homegirl Tinchy from my B&B days. She told me to link her at her new hostel, round the corner in Hackney Wick. I left my car outside my mum's, put my gun in an empty video case and walked over.

When I got there I saw Aaron and Havoc, two older Fields boys, standing outside. I weren't watching no face, doh, I went to my first rave with Aaron when I was eleven years old. Things had changed a lot since then so I didn't say nothing to him. I gave Havoc a spud, and said, "What? You can't say wah gwarn, nah?"

I wondered why Havoc wouldn't say 'hello'. This same guy used to be in my yard on a daily when I lived in Holly Street. I thought he was my brother's bredrin. I had to keep reminding myself that everyone from Hackney was a Fields boy now. I was the enemy to everyone I grew up with - Totty boys, Fields boys and a few Holly Street boys. I shook my head, kissed my teeth and went inside the yard to see Tinchy.

Me and her chilled and smoked weed until late. The noise in the hostel got loud. Tinchy went to see what it was all about. She returned with fear in her eyes. "Listen Robyn, all them Fields boys are in here. And they're having a drink-up, downstairs. I never knew." The drink-up was to do with Jadie's funeral the next day. I couldn't believe my bad luck. What will be, will be.

Tinchy was so scared she phoned my brother. He drove down to get me. When he reached he phoned from his car. I made my way down, slowly, my gun in the video case. I couldn't believe how many

Fields boys were there. They were everywhere. Even outside, sitting on both sides of the concrete staircase leading up to the front door. They were about forty-man strong. A couple of the olders who I had always seen as neutrals in the Holly Street and Fields beef, were giving me dirty looks so I did the same. Funny how when I'm outnumbered man wanna get brave. But when certain man are by themself and they see me one they ain't sayin nothing. Kiss my fucking teeth.

I got in the car with my brother. The whole crew was watching. We watched them back. A lot of the olders used to be bless with my brother. Now they were looking like they forgot dem days. We drove away slowly. Very slowly. After a short distance we stopped at the lights. My phone rang. It was Tinchy. She sounded shook. "Robyn, I just heard them say, they're gonna move to you," she whispered down the phone.

"All right. Calm down. Don't worry." I hung up.

We were still at the lights. I looked in the rear view mirror and saw Fields boys going into the boot of their cars. Some jumped into cars and pulled up behind us. I told my brother to buss the lights but he didn't care. "If they're serious, Rob, let them do what they gotta do."

The lights changed and they started driving dodgy behind us. I took my gun to the window but my brother pushed my arm down. "Robyn, calm the fuck down. They're not serious."

He had no intention of speeding up for none of them. Two cars breezed past, but he weren't watching that. He just eased into the estate towards Hartlake. We pulled over and a next car drove past slowly. The boys inside looked at us and carried on. And that was it. For whatever reason no shoot-out was needed that night and, thank God, I was safe again.

A part of me wanted to go to Jadie's funeral and pay my respects. I wasn't crazy enough to. Emotions would be high and things could kick off. I would never forgive myself if I disrespected anyone's funeral. Mum told my brother to go and pay respects on my behalf. Afterwards he met me in Holly Street. "Rob, your boy J got a decent send-off. One man tried to give me screw face in church but I wasn't even watching that joker."

I went back to Wolverhampton, alive and in one piece. I had made it through to another birthday - just about.

FAITH IN THE SYSTEM OR FAITH

Before I left for London to face my judgment, I met up with Jackie from church again. She told me that they were still praying for me. I found it hard to pray for myself. At this time in my life, God wasn't the thing or person I would call on to have my back. My faith in God got shattered some time ago. I asked him to save my Nan's life, and he weren't saying nothing. I didn't have faith in Him or justice. Regardless of how I felt I still bowed down on my knees and asked God for mercy. But it felt like I was chatting to myself. One night as I was catching a vibe, my phone rang.

It was my girl "Are you all right, babes?" she asked.

"Yeah, I'm good. You?"

"Errm... I've got something to tell you."

"What's wrong?" The tone in her voice weren't right.

"I'm pregnant."

I paused. "Cool, whatever you decide, I got you." I was lost for words. I wasn't ready to be a father. I was still a yute. I'd got nothing to offer a child. There ain't no guarantee I'll be on road when the baby's due. Shit, if I go to jail I'm gonna be just like my dad was, ghost. This is some bollocks. How can I be a dad if I'm not even on road? Let me bill a ziggy and watch some Bernie Mac.

October 2003 and I was back in London. I drove with my girl to Wood Green Crown Court. My case was set for a three-day hearing. I was put in the dock to listen to the evidence against me. The so-called victim, Kaiya, wasn't there. When I asked my barrister why, he whispered that Kaiya was doing time and would be temporarily released to give evidence against me on the third day. This snitch was violating the rules. How can you be a bad boy in prison but still be snitching on man? What the fuck?

Up in court, I saw the boy's mum and sister. They were with some next muscle man giving me bare dirty looks. I had to smile it off to keep calm. I turned to Od'z from the docks and said, "Look at this old G, with his sleeveless top." I didn't know who the man was, all I knew is that he was trying his best to intimidate me, dressed in black, his arms crossed, like he's some type of contract killer. To stay calm I had to make a joke of it. "Od'z, I beg you lend my man over there a t-shirt." I fronted like I was in the mood for running joke, but really I wanted to jump out the dock and hit the hit man.

They were looking down on me like I was a no-good piece of worthless shit. Maybe they thought their boy Kaiya was some innocent bystander, who got stabbed for no reason.

Kaiya and his snitch friends jumped my boy Darker. Kaiya ain't no rarse angel. He's a fucking road man, just like me. And now this same brudder's tryna get me birded off, yeah? Alrite watch what I do if I catch man in jail.

I was standing in the docks looking at a sentence from 7-15. But there weren't no victims that night, just a casualty of war. He had no right to snitch, just coz he nearly lost his life. Beef is beef, it's not personal. These snitches are just badmind.

Day two of the trial was more or less the same - tension, dirty looks and snitches giving evidence against me. Then judgment day. I kept thinking the worse. I couldn't remember the last time I saw a black boy go to court for a verdict and come back out?

The little faith I had was fading. I mumbled a prayer. I stood in the dock looking at his family, thinking, if I go down for this, I'll have to keep it real to the end. Tension was building. The court put a special procedure in place so the jury didn't know Kaiya was a prisoner and they wouldn't be prejudiced against him. We were ushered out of the courtroom and brought back in fifteen minutes later. It was a good thing they did it like that. Real talk. The way I was feeling, if I had to watch him walk past, I would have slapped him.

I was standing in the dock with a guard either side of me. I turned towards my girl and noticed her three month belly popping out. My heart was burning. I wanted to punch-up every witness for trying to deny my yute a father figure and make me look as bad as the man who was never there for me growing up.

At last, I got to see Kaiya, the boy who I was accused of trying to kill. After he hugged his Mum he turned around and gave me the wickedest look. I couldn't believe the way this brudder's looking at me. Like say he's some bad bwoy on road. When the evidence of his blood-stained clothes was shown to the court he broke down. At first he couldn't even speak. For a split second, I felt the brother's pain. I can't explain what it was, but when I saw him drop a tear I felt something different inside. Not pity or nothing like that, but it was far from hatred. Then he switched and started to shout out and cry.

It wasn't the shouting that grabbed my attention. If I'm honest, after I saw him drop a tear nothing made sense. Any fool could see the tear he dropped was half genuine. My brain was hurting with confusion. Why is this bad boy crying, and still screwing me down?

Kaiya finally finished giving evidence against me. At last I got the chance to say my side of the story. Then I had to deal with the prosecution trying to bury me alive. The way the prosecutor was shouting at me you would have thought I did him something.

Kaiya's prosecutor was chatting bare shit. I sat in the dock quietly and didn't say a word while all the snitches were telling lies about me. The second I tried to talk someone shouted out, "He's a liar." When I looked to my left, through the glass all I could see was bare heads shaking. Kaiya's family didn't wanna hear a word I had to say.

Who were they to say I'm lying? They weren't even there. Oh yeah, of course...everyone thinks their kid does no wrong.

Not long after I sat down, it was time to stand up again for judgment. The moment of truth had come. The judge asked the foreman of the jury:

"On the charge of the attempted murder of Kaiya Truman, how do you find the defendant?"

The jury replied: "Not Guilty." "Brap! Brap!"

I was in shock. All I heard was 'guilty' and my bredrin Od'z shout, "Brap! Brap!" Then one of the guards turned to me and said, "You're free to go."

That's when it sank in. The tension was still high when I walked out of the courtroom with my girl. Janet gave me a hug. All of my people were pleased for me. I was smiling coz I was a free man.

"You almost killed my son. And you're standing there smiling," Kaiya's mum shouted at me.

I was brought up to respect my elders so I wasn't going to diss her. I just looked at her and calmly said, "You need to check your son. He's a very angry young man and he aint no angel himself."

We went back to my girlfriend's mum's house in Totty. I felt blessed, like a heavy weight was lifted off my shoulders. Now all I have to do is stay out of trouble for the next six months and I'm gonna get the chance to see the birth of my first yute. And, maybe one day, change my life round for good. I'm due to be a father I can't be repping the streets no more.

Back in Wolverhampton I phoned Jackie and told her I was found not guilty. She was overjoyed and we both thanked God. It's only right. God knows what happened that day. I guess praying helps after all.

I was feeling positive about the future and felt like I finally had a fresh start. I rang my girl and told her to pack her bags and move up to Wolverhampton with me. But that plan flopped. She weren't feeling that idea. We were both young and about to have our first child and we wouldn't have any support in Wolverhampton. When she said "support" that straight-up hurt my pride. I didn't care 'bout none of that crap. I don't rely on no one.

I'm big 18 now, I don't need no rarse support. What's my girl really saying? That I'm not capable of looking after us alone? She might have had a point. I was barely getting by myself and now I had to provide for a newborn. Shit. I had made plans doh. I had gone to look at courses at Wolverhampton College and I had applied for a job at the local Royal Mail. I never saw myself as no wasteman, I was getting ready for mine.

Fuck it, I ain't going back to London to risk my life and freedom - that's long. Being in an area where nobody knew me gave me some peace of mind. I didn't have to watch my back.

Real talk, doh, I needed to think about this one properly. I didn't want the streets to stop me from being a full-time father. I wanted to be there for my child daily. I really couldn't see it any other way.

THE PROMISE WITHIN THE SACRIFICE

After a week of smoking weed and praying about it, I decided to return to London - the last place I wanted to be at the time. Most of the Holly Street boys were still in prison, and Jadie's death was still fresh in the air. For my child's sake, I had to go back. The day before I left Wolverhampton, I held my Nan's photo and made a promise to try my best to be a good father and leave the badness behind. It didn't make sense beefing with man over which area they came from any more. Coming from the roads we got life hard enough already. Why continue to make it harder by beefing a man just like me over his address? Shit! What had I been doing all these years?

My view on this road life was finally changing but my temper weren't. Some old G close to me said, "Rob, best ting you do is keep your gun in east London and the bullets in west. That way, if you lose your temper on road, you'll have time to calm down before you get trigger happy." The old G was tryna save me from myself. I rated that highly. But it wasn't enough. I wasn't the type of yute that would calm down in the time it takes to get to west from east. Nah, I needed to be gun free. So I got rid of my knives, my gun and, I told myself, time to give up the skunk too. I said a final prayer, jumped in my car and hit the M1.

By November I was living at my girl's house in Totty. A big risk. I can't deny I feared for my life, but I made the sacrifice for my unborn child and stepped out on a new ounce of faith. I wanted to believe God would have my back because he could see I was trying to be a good yute.

After a few months back I linked up with Woodz in Hackney. He was going to one dance up in Oxford and wanted me to roll with him. I got in his car and he drove to Holly Street to pick up Risky Talent. When we reached, Marcus was there too. I wasn't too bothered because he and I had a reasoned a few weeks earlier about our little beef. I told him straight up that he should have never brought a knife to my Nan's house and that's why I stabbed him. In his defence Marcus said, "I wasn't gonna stab you. Fam, I brought the knife just in case."

I thought, this boy's head's not right. It didn't even make sense trying to explain to him where he was wrong. He really didn't get it. 'Bout, Oh I weren't gonna stab you. What the fuck? "Marcus, you for real, bruv? You don't bring a knife hidden up your sleeve for your friend - just in case. Whatever, innit, dead that argument. One more thing, you weren't involved in the Jadie thing was you?"

"Nah."

"Alright say nothing, beef squashed."

And that was the end of the beef between us. If I still had my old mentality, I probably would have found it hard to squash the beef. But now I was going to be a father and felt like I had to man up and make a transition.

When we got to the rave I kept to myself. I still felt strange about being near Marcus. It just didn't feel like the old days but I got on with it. When the dance was over, we stood outside. It was blitz. Marcus didn't have a jacket. And just like the old days, Risky Talent, and dem man started running joke on him. I had two jackets on me and I didn't feel no way about lending Marcus one to wear, coz it was fucking cold. Even though I forgave him fully he was still the same person. So I weren't trying to be all pally-pally with him. The second we got back to London we went our separate ways without any hard feelings between us.

PROMISES TO KEEP

April 2004 and the special day finally came. My son was born. It was one of them sunny days where you can't see a cloud in the sky. The first time I set eyes on mini me the world just paused. It didn't even kick in.

Rah, I got a son now, madness. Gotta fix up for real now. I had a new hunger to change, and new dreams to make happen. I was ready to divorce the streets for good. I didn't give a damn about any past beef any more. Now I finally had a reason to love my life. I just wanted to do the best I could for little man. A promise is a comfort to a fool, but I wouldn't let him go through half the bullshit I went through. Promise.

I found it hard adjusting to this new life. The one promise I couldn't keep was the giving up weed. What can I say? This shit helps me deal with the pain.

It was sometime in August 2004, and one of my old Holly Street boys was touching the roads again. It really don't matter what streets you come from. It's just standard to get excited when you see one of your brothers land road. Geezer just finished doing a bird for some next madness. During his time away, I wrote and visited him. Around that time he gave me his personal reason for why he took Marcus's side that night. I weren't fully feeling it but fuck what I feel, everyone's entitled to their opinion.

On the day he was released, I went to Fresh field in Holly Street to go welcome him home. When I got there, he was sitting next to Raiden on the park fence. I hailed out couple of the Rowdy Bunch boys - Red Eye and Temper, who I was cool with. I said "Wah gwarn" to everyone. Except for Marcus, because he had a hoody covering his face and seemed to be upset about something. He was bopping up and down like some mad man. No one paid him any mind. I couldn't understand why he was wearing a hooded jacket coz it was baking outside. I jumped on the fence and sat next to my bredrins. We all started running joke. Geezer couldn't believe I had a yute. He found it funny that I was a father now coz before he went jail I was living a different life, saying different things.

As I sat there expressing my joy with da mandem, I felt a punch in my leg. I was sitting so high up on the fence that I almost fell back. I held on to the fence to get my balance. When I looked down I saw Marcus stabbing me in the leg. I pushed myself back over the fence. That's when I realised that he had just snaked me. I couldn't believe it. I ran round the corner shouting, "Marcus, you're dead. You're dead!"

I stole a knife from someone's house. On my way back I saw my brother. I jumped in his car and went back to carve up Marcus. It hadn't even been three minutes but when I returned to the scene Marcus was ghost - nowhere to be seen. "Where's the pussy' ole gone?" I shouted.

Man there started acting like I was some foreigner asking for directions. What the fuck? Them man, are meant to be cool with both me and Marcus. How can they watch him snake me like that and not say a word? All of a sudden no one knows what direction he ran off in? Fuckery. Geezer was the biggest hypocrite. When I stabbed Marcus three years earlier, Geezer was the first to bark at me, "Rob, what's wrong with you, how can you stab him?" He even did the righteous thing that night and took Marcus to the hospital. But now that the shoe was on the other foot and Marcus just stabbed me, Geezer weren't saying a word. He wouldn't even tell me which way Marcus had run. It finally hit home. I don't know why he took sides, but that shit hurt.

I went to the hospital with Likkle Vicious then back to my girl's house. She could see I was mad. I had to ignore the sounds of my son crying, and I tried to not forget the promise I made him to behave. But I thought: fuck that, I'm licking it down. I had to put my son to the back of my mind to lick down Marcus. What upset me most was the snakey way he stabbed me. I struggled to find a good enough reason not to kill Marcus. I knew him like the back and front of my hand. Someone from Holly Street must have pressured him into doing it.

The temptation to retaliate was unbearable. Before I became a father I wouldn't have thought twice about revenge. The only thing that might have stopped me was the risk of getting caught. I had a rep to maintain. A million and one thoughts went through my mind as I battled with my ego. I was vex.

I got Marcus's number and phoned him. When he answered I said, "You're a snake y'know, pussy. Since when you turn so snakey? I don't have time to play games with you, bruv. I hope you're feeling proud, bad man."

"Nah, I don't feel better," he said. "I thought I would, but I don't."

Whata clown. As much as I wanted revenge he really wasn't worth going jail for. I lost all respect for him. Instead of making him pay with his life I swallowed my pride and got on with it. It was a minor. I tried my best not to lose sleep over it. Somehow, I woke up the next morning laughing about it.

Later that week I had all smiles wiped off my face. I got a phone call from a friend, who told me that my boy Dudus was dead. Dudus's body was found floating in the River Thames by London Bridge. I went alone to his funeral a few weeks later. He was laid to rest in Manor Park Cemetery, East London. Apparently he had committed suicide. How, when he was so strong mentally? Dudus was a bless brother. He was a Clapton Square boy but he never took ownership of any postcode, nor did he rep one. That's what made Dudus different from most of us. Dudus was just Dudus.

To get my mind off all of this death shit, I started boxing down at Islington boys club. Soon after I ended up at Haringey boxing club in

Tottenham. I was getting really fit and decided to stop smoking for good.

Training was hard work but they said I was a natural fighter. It was a good way to help get rid of anger and frustrations. Around this time, me, my son and his mum were living in Bruce Grove, next to Broadwater Farm in Tottenham. I never imagined I would be raising my yute in Totty. Especially as many people still saw me as a Hackney man through and through. I wasn't comfortable living in the area at all. I hated walking on road there. Inside the house it felt like home, but outside it was clearly Tottenham.

As much as I didn't like jammin with some Holly Street boys, it was better than being in Tottenham all day every day. I found myself spending nuff time in E8. I still didn't trust or talk to half of da mandem, but that shit didn't keep me away. Holly Street was like some magnet drawing me in. I just couldn't let it go. It made me who I am - a fighter. Other than all the pain and injustice I felt, I can honestly say that some of the best days of my life were spent in Holly Street. Especially the time I spent living with Nan.

September 2004. I decided that enough was enough. I enrolled in a sports science course in South West London. One morning, about a week into the course, I was standing outside the class when my phone rang. It was Diamond. God knows why he was belling me so early.

"Wha gwarn, D. You good? Why you phoning man at these GMTV times." There was no response. So I said, "Yo, shout me back at lunch time, I'm late for a lesson."

"Didn't you hear, Trav?" "Hear what?"

"It's Mintz, bruv, he's dead. He got shot in the head last night."

I was stunned. I dashed my rucksack and sat on the floor. I tried to soldier it and walk into the lesson, but after a few seconds I thought, Fuck college. I left and never went back.

Mintz's death was just as big a shock to me as Jadie's and Dudus'. As far as I know, Mintz didn't have no enemies. He had bare man hating on him, but not enemies. Mintz was the real fresh prince of Hackney. Our birthdays were only a week apart. Maybe that's the reason we got along so well. We never argued or fought once. Mintz never told me until we were long good friends that the first time he met me he was supposed to fight me. He said his older brother offered him money to beat me up coz he didn't like Big Trav and I'm too facety. But when he met me himself he said he thought I was bless so he didn't listen to his brother. When he told me that I had to laugh.

I can't lie, when Mintz died it messed me up inside. But I had to bury my feelings because I wasn't sure how he really felt about me before he departed. He was still friends with Marcus who stabbed me just the month before. I had to ask myself if Mintz still saw me as a bredrin before he left us. But he was there for me when I was taken into care. That meant just as much as someone having my back in a beef. I'll never forget Mintz. Bless for that brother.

At his funeral, I walked up to where he lay peacefully to say my final goodbyes. "God, where are you now? I can't see you again." Later that day, Mintz was buried at Manor Park Cemetery. I started to get this strange feeling that my other friend Dudus, who was buried a couple months earlier, was buried somewhere local to where Mintz was being buried. I looked around and saw Dudus' grave metres away. Madness. He was buried only eleven gravestones away from Mintz. On the same row too. How the fuck can I have two friends, who used to play computer in my bedroom, buried a few metres apart?

After the burial I went to the reception in a pub. I kept myself to myself because I weren't on begging friend with no one. I can't even front, it was surreal. Five years earlier, me, Mintz and the rest of the Holly Street mandem used to all be one big family. We jammed with each other all day and every day. Reminders like that were adding to my hurt and constant confusion.

I couldn't understand why brothers I was bless with had to die so young like this. Everyone else in the crew were still friends. Some-times being alone was hard. I was directly across da mandem jamming, the only thing between us was a snooker table. Likkle Vicious and Woodz were on my side of the table when Red Eye came up to me.

"Wah gwarn, Rob? You good?" he said. "Yeah Redz, I'm bless. You?"

"Yeah, Robs, you know that man are saying you're a Fields boy. And that you were there at Jadie's funeral."

"I ain't no Fields boy. That's a remix. I would've liked to be at his funeral to pay my respects, doh. I don't give a fuck what no one thinks, he was my boy still. Red-Eye, which ever man's saying that, tell them come move to me next time they see me." Chups!

After hearing those rumours I felt a way. I couldn't wait to get home, back to Totty, to get out of this suit. Even though no one said it to my face, I felt that I wasn't welcome at the funeral.

I got home feeling drained. I was sick and tired of being painted like some Judas. It was the worst feeling ever. I couldn't cry or mourn for none of my dead friends. I was seen as the bad guy on both sides of E8. I wanted to get away for good and never come back. Fuck life. At least I wouldn't have to carry this pain no more.

I lit the candle that was given to me at the funeral. I said a prayer for Mintz and his family, then I went to sleep. I woke up the next morning angry, battling emotions. I couldn't allow myself to feel hurt. It only made me feel angry and bitter. So instead I worked on blocking out the whole E8 experience. Forever.

CHANGE AIN'T AS EASY YOU THINK

It had been a year since Mintz's death and I was getting more serious and focused about boxing. I finally took myself away from anything to do with the streets. I was going to put all my anger, frustration, and negative emotion into boxing. After training for a year I was well ready for my first fight. I had my medical, made the weight for the fight, and was fired up to go. The big debut was a cold November night in 2005. And I was representing Tottenham for the Haringey Boxing Club. I had to crack a smile when I heard the commentator shout in the mic.

"And in the blue corner, representing Tottenham, Haringey Boxing Club... Robyn Travis!"

I mumbled a prayer, touched gloves with my opponent, then we got it cracking.

At first I stuck to the game plan and somehow knocked him down early. As I was standing over him he tried to throw a punch or something. I almost lost my temper and went to stamp it out. But the ref came and pushed me away. All I could hear was the whole room full of people shouting, "Calm down, Robyn, calm down."

Then I heard the voice of my one year old son repeating the same thing, "Calm down, Robyn." My corner man, Brian, told me to leave all that street stuff in the streets and show my skills. So that's exactly what I did. I came out boxing properly and caught him with haymakers that made the crowd shout "oooohhh". This guy was taking a beating but he was as hard as nails. I caught him with a wild right. He was dazed and started to run for it.

When I saw that, I was on him like butter on toast. The ref pushed me off again and started counting. Before he got to ten, the man said, "I'm done, I'm done."

For the first time in my life I was proud of myself. I proved I was still a man. I didn't need a knife or a gun to show the heart I've got. All it took was hard work and discipline.

Two days later I was back at the gym training for my next fight. I didn't know what I wanted to do with my life but I liked how boxing was changing me. I had a date with destiny, it was time to overcome my fears. A couple weeks later I was matched up for two more fights. I was ready and in the zone. I was sparring daily with some great boxers. The club was filled with young stars in the making. And I wanted to be up there. Repping.

As I was sparring an old injury came back to haunt me. I went to the hospital and was told that I couldn't box until I had an operation on my elbow. This was a massive blow for me. I couldn't train properly because of the pain so I slowly started to get fed up.

I couldn't sit at home feeling like some wasteman so I started looking for a job again. Six months passed and I weren't having any luck whatsoever. Another summer had reached, it was July 2006. I needed qualifications bad, but I couldn't face starting another college course to drop out again. I managed to get two job interviews by my own efforts, but I got turned down coz of my lack of qualifications and experience. These employers were upsetting my spirit. How do they expect anyone to have experience if they don't want to hire them so they can gain it? Having a criminal record didn't help either.

The Job Centre sent me to Reed in Partnership to help me look for work but I had so many doors shut in my face I was beginning to think they couldn't help me either. After a few weeks, they got me a job interview with the betting agency Ladbrokes. The day after the interview, Reed called me and told me I was successful. I was happy that I got given a chance to make an honest living. The following day I went to Reed in Partnership to sign off. When I got there my personal advisor called me into a room for a chat.

"Between me and you, bruv," he said, "I think my colleague has swapped your file with one of her clients. I think she done it because she's not hitting her targets to get her clients into employment."

"Okay, so what you saying?"

"Sorry, Rob, but you haven't got the job, mate."

"What do you mean 'sorry'? Tell your manager."

He said if he told his manager he might lose his job for leaving my file unattended. He seemed like a cool guy and, as pissed as I was, I didn't want him to lose his job over me. So I didn't bother to pursue it.

Back at home money was getting tight. We were also getting threatened with eviction letters. One evening we were eating dinner and my two year old was thirsty. We had no juice in the house so his mum gave him some tap water. He took a sip of it, threw it on the floor and said, "I want juice. Juice!"

I wanted to slap his skin off that second for being so ungrateful. But I had to remind myself that he's barely two years old and doesn't even know what ungrateful means. I felt like I was failing as a father. I felt like I was such a wasteman. I didn't even have £2.00 to rub together to buy a box juice. I remembered the promise I made when my son was born, that I wouldn't let him go through any of the bad stuff I went through when I was growing up. The fear of facing the humiliation of eviction again haunted me. But I didn't want to resort to the streets – I had to think of something else.

One day I was in Holly Street speaking to a family member about the eviction letters. He started telling me I could make some quick money by bringing drugs back from Jamaica.

I laughed. "No way. That's a bate ting."

"Nah fam," he said. "Trust me. Proper tings. I went out there myself. It's my people doing it. They pay for your flight and stay, and if Operation Kingfish is on then the whole thing gets called off. That's what happened to me and so I enjoyed the pleasure of a free holiday and spending money."

It was a close family member so I trusted him. With those eviction letters in mind, I told him to link me up with his people. My flight was booked, and I had three weeks to go before I was due to fly out to Jamaica. At first I wasn't sure about going through with it, but when I linked up with one of the main people, I saw that it was my brother's friend, Brenda. I felt much more at ease coz I knew she wouldn't lead me astray. She had watched me grow up and, in a way, she was just like family. I kept praying about it and vowed, if I get a steady job before my flight to Jamaica, I won't need to do that move.

Two weeks after agreeing to go I was speaking to the manager of my old boxing club in Islington. He told me that he was now the manager and owner of a plumbing and electrical company in Hornsey and that I should come and do some work for a day. If I was good enough he would keep me on. I went to his office and was taken by the assistant manager to a house in Golders Green to do some electrician work, which I had never done before. The assistant manager left me with some other foreign workers and told me to follow their instructions. And do exactly what they told me to do. Then he left. It was 6pm by the time the work had finished. I was so tired coz I had worked my arse off to impress. I really wanted to get this job so I could provide for my family.

The assistant manager came back and was making a big scene. He questioned the other workers about my work and criticised everything I had done. The other workers looked to me in disbelief. They shrugged their shoulders and shook their heads. The assistant manager carried on effing and blinding, then he jumped in his van and left me behind in Golders Green. After he'd gone, the other workers told me that there was nothing wrong with the work I did. They couldn't understand why he was behaving like that.

I made my own way back to the office in Hornsey. I went to speak to the manager who offered me the day's trial to personally tell him how the day went. But he said, "Robyn, my assistant told me he wasn't happy with your work. So I can't give you the job."

I got angry, but in a firm and respectful way, and gave him my side of the story. I walked out the office with this strange feeling that this cockney assistant manager was a racist prat who just didn't want me to work there. I left angry and upset.

When I got back to Tottenham, there was a letter saying that the operation for my boxing injury was due in a few months. That eased my anger. At least I would be able to start boxing again soon.

SECOND THOUGHTS

It was a week until my trip and I didn't want to do it any more. I wanted to make an honest living. I had applied to the London Fire Brigade. I still hadn't heard anything but I prayed daily and begged God to provide me with an opportunity to avoid doing anything illegal. Two days before I was due to fly, I got the form from the LFB. God had answered my prayers. It was only an application form, but I took it as a sign that I should cancel the trip. I called Brenda and told her to call it off.

"It's cool if you don't wanna go ahead with it," she said. "But the tickets have been paid for, and we're not gonna get a refund. So if you wanna just go for a holiday, then you can go for free."

"Sorry for the last minute change, sis, but my heart's not on it. I fully appreciate the holiday - I need one."

I packed a few vests, shorts and my boxing gear so I could train while I was out there. I was good to go. The day before my flight my cousin called me and we argued about me changing my mind. "You shouldn't mess people about," he said. "Saying you'll do it one minute then changing your mind the next."

"All right, cool, but Brenda said it weren't a big problem, fam. I'm just going for the holiday."

The conversation got heated. My cousin felt that since I wasn't going to do the 'drugs run' that I shouldn't take up the offer of a free holiday, because I didn't really know the people. I couldn't see what the problem was if Brenda said it was okay. The argument didn't really get anywhere as we were both shouting over each other. So I hung up.

WELCOME TO JAMROCK

In august '06 I flew out to sunny Jamaica. When I touched down, there was no-one there to meet me. I was pissed. I had a little change, but not enough for a hotel. After thinking the worst, a black jeep pulled up beside me. It was Brenda's people. They bussed opened the boot so I could fling down my suitcase, then I jumped in the back and we drove in total silence. We finally arrived and they left me to unpack.

The apartment was nothing special. One room, a kitchen and a bathroom. I woke up to a wicked sunrise the next day and went for my daily jog on the beach. I finished off with some circuit training. I kinda felt good about myself. Back at the apartment, I was having a shower when I heard a knock at the door. It was a tall Jamaican man called Richie, another one of Brenda's people. He wanted to reason with me. He was trying to persuade me to change my mind about taking the drugs back to England. Richie seemed like a cool brudder. Way cooler than the two who brought me from the airport.

"Nah bruv, I'm good," I told him. "That's not for me right now. I'm here to train and get my mind right."

"Cool, nah man, but try tink 'bout it still," he said.

"Nah, G. My mind's not changing. That shit's bate right now, especially with the recent terrorist checks."

"Nuh worry 'bout dat. We have the ting on lock and key. If yuh change yuh mind, just know seh we have the link at the airport. Yuh 'ear dat?"

The next day Richie came to the apartment and we went out raving in some ghetto-looking area. My routine was more or less the same every day - training in the morning, raving at night. I had two days left in J.A. When Richie made a final attempt to persuade me. This time he was aggressive, like he was putting it on man. These hustlers weren't gonna take no for an answer. They were acting like they might do me something if I didn't agree to go through with it. What the fuck? I thought these were my people's people. The man could see I wanted to punch his face in. But then I also wanted to get back home in one piece.

I agreed to do it and Richie explained how the whole thing was going to go down.

"Me ah guh cut open de suitcase and put a likkle amount ah drugs inna it, an' then put some coffee beans round it fi disguise de smell from de sniff a dawg dem," he said. "Then, me ahguh bring back de suitcase inna de morning so you cyan pack yuh clothes inna it. Then, when it time fi leave, me will sen a driva fi cum pick up yuh and de suitcase. T'ree o'clock sharp! When yuh get fi de airport, de driva ah guh tek yuh suitcase to ah allocatid worker at de check-in desk. De allocatid worker ah guh hensure dat yuh suitcase mek it pon de plane widout a search." He paused. "De only risk is when yuh pick back up yuh suitcase inna Hengland. We have no control over dat."

There weren't gonna be no rarse picking up suitcases back in England. I just wanted those snakes off my back.

The night before departure my spirit felt uneasy. The temptation to pick up the suitcase back in England was now in me. I tried to pray against the temptation but I couldn't. I kept thinking about those eviction letters and the fact that no one wanted to give me a job back home.

My day to leave Jamaica had come. Just as Richie said, the driver came to pick me at three o'clock sharp. He put the suitcase in the boot and I jumped in the car. We got to Montego Bay airport in good time for check-in. The driver took the suitcase and passed it to the allocated member of staff at the desk. He then winked at me and walked off.

Moments later, the allocated worker at the check-in desk asked me for a departure lounge fee. I was baffled. I didn't even know what the hell that was. But I had to play it cool. I searched my pockets for change, but I was a few dollars short. I turned behind me and asked a Jamaican man if he could lend me a few dollars until we landed back in England. I was blessed that this kind man lent me the money without hesitation. I smiled but was pissed off. Brenda's people were fucking slippin'! They should've known that I had to pay a fee. Chups! Why is this guy at the desk asking me for the fee, if he's supposed to be in on it? I kept thinking the worst, but told myself not to worry. Maybe it was just a minor slip-up.

I lined up to board the plane, and as the line got shorter, I noticed a tall white man checking passports. Hell, no! That's an undercover fed, and he looks English. Operation Kingfish!

I was overly pissed, but I tried to style it out by running joke with another passenger in the line. I weren't even listening to his reply. I just faked a smile whilst praying in my mind.

God, 'llow me, man. I need to make it on this plane. Beg you don't let this officer pick me out. I promise I won't touch that suitcase when I get back to England. I'll leave that shit behind. Promise.

When I got to the front of the queue, the British officer looked at my passport. Then he asked me and another black girl from England to wait in next room for a minute. Everything seemed like a dream at that moment, but I needed to stay on point. In the room I asked the girl if she had drugs in her suitcase and she said, "No way". By this time I knew my suitcase was going to be searched, so I gave her a tiny piece of paper with Janet's number on. Just in case things didn't work out for the best. The girl nodded and started to look shit scared for me.

Jamaican policemen entered the room and escorted me to the plane, where my suitcase was on the ground. They asked if the suitcase was mine. "Yes," I said. The suitcase was surrounded by sniffer dogs going crazy, so they decided to cut it open. Two officers began searching it. It didn't take long before they both shouted.

"Bludfyah!"

"That's a lot ah drugs, my yute! Did you know about this?"

"No way. That's not mine," I said.

I made a scene like I was really surprised. When they took me back to the room, one of the officers smiled and said, "You're a young bwoy, and it's sad coz you're gonna be in prison here fi a very long time. That's a lot of drugs."

"They're not mine," I shouted.

I was handcuffed, taken to Montego Bay jail house and put on remand. Before I was even placed in my cell, I had learnt the lesson. I didn't need punishing for this. Once again I had failed. But this time I had failed my son, and anyone else who genuinely gave a fuck about me.

PRISON'S NOT A BED OF ROSES

I was escorted down a dark passageway lined with cells packed with women prisoners in total darkness. I could hear them but I couldn't see them. They could see me and they started calling out through the bars.

"Wot you lot in for," I called back.

"Murder!", "Murder!", "Murder!", "Murder!" It sounded like an echo but with different voices.

They immediately heard the difference in my voice. "What's a young, good-looking bwoy like you doing lock-up inna Jamaica?" I heard someone call. "Baby love, please, me beg yuh, be careful down dere," someone else said, "becaw nuff man dead inna de mandem section, yuh nah. And know seh yuh ah guh bawl out yuh eye dem tonight."

"Nah love, not me. Man don't do the crying ting," I managed to say before the sharp shove of my prison escort pushed me on.

The further we went the more grimey it looked and the louder the screaming became in the section of the jail that I would later find out the inmates and the screws had nicknamed 'Vietnam'. My escort didn't flinch at the murderous screams coming from 'Nam'; he'd heard it all before. Finally we were outside the overcrowded hell hole that would be my new home. Immediately I got into an argument with a couple other prisoners in the passageway as I waited for the screw to open the cell door.

"Yo, wha yuh av fi me?" the first one said.

"Me hear seh you box," the next one said. "Me ah go fix some shower fight fe yuh. Mek money, my yute."

"Sorry, cuz, I don't fight black people," I said.

He didn't find it funny one bit. Then I turned to the short man who asked me if I had anything for him. I had to bite my lip to stop myself kicking him down for trying to rob me.

If these man think I'm some dickhead they better think again. I'm not having it, star.

The prison guard then shoved me inside the cell. Darkness you can adjust to, but there is no getting used to a cell the size of two double mattresses. A concrete ledge on each wall was the closest thing to a bed. This cell was home to fourteen men. I made it fifteen. It was suffocating and it stunk like gone off chicken and weed in there. By now I had figured out why the guard handed me a piece of cardboard. A few inmates were sleeping on similar 'beds'. I 'made' mine in the only available spot, right by the toilet. I curled up in the fetal position and lay my head on my rolled up jumper and tried to get some sleep but roaches were crawling all over me.

One of my cell mates started laughing his head off. "Chucky, what's so funny?" someone said.

"De Henglish bwoy. I man never see nobody come inna de cell so calm like 'im...Yo, Henglish bwoy. Yuh bin 'ere before?"

All the mandem in the cell started laughing. "Nah, never flown to yard before," I said. "But any time old bill lock me up back home, first thing I do is sleep."

"Why?" Chucky asked.

"Coz the sooner it starts, the sooner it will finish."

From somewhere in the darkness an English voice asked where I was from.

"Hackney," I said.

"Cool," the voice said. "Me and my brother here are from South. Streatham." His name was Screwface. He and his brother, Norm, were in their forties. They confirmed my belief that this prison is hell on earth. "Prepare yourself for the worst," Norm said.

I woke up the next morning as hungry as hell. We weren't fed the night before. When I heard a man say "Breakfast time!" I was grinning bare teeth. As soon as the screws opened the cell door the inmates ran out like the cell was on fire. I ran with them, almost tasting the cornmeal porridge before I had even tried it, certain that breakfast was gonna be nice if it gets that reaction from the prison mandem. I stopped licking my lips the second I was out the cell door. The sight of one of the inmates dragging a big nasty bucket across the filthy corridor floor had me standing there baffed. I soon clocked that the nasty bucket was filled with tea. The same inmate was handing everyone a single slice of bread. His hands didn't look too clean either.

A single slice of bread and one cup of tea caused the mandem to rush like that! Where the fuck am I? I didn't have a cup, so I could only get a slice of bread. Beggars can't be choosers.

I thought slavery days were over. I learned the hard way that this jail didn't supply prisoners with anything. And I do mean anything.

Back in the cell, making the most of my slice of hard dough, the brothers from South London asked me if I had family in Jamaica.

"Nah, my mum's family's from Barbados."

"And your dad?"

"I really don't know."

The brothers warned me that if I didn't have family bringing me food, or money for food, I was going to suffer big time. "You've got to make the most of what you get in here," Screwface said. "Even if it's only a slice of bread and a cup of tea. Most inmates only get to eat anything else if someone from the outside brings them food."

Food always came from a bucket. Three times a day:

Meal 1) 08.00 - A single slice of hard dough bread

Meal 2) 13.00 - Chickenfoot

Meal 3) 16.00 - Dinner time. Stale callaloo and hard rice

That was it. Unless, like I said, someone brought you food on visits. In which case you could eat like a king. I was a few days into my remand time when hunger and stress started to kick in. It was like we had no human rights whatsoever. I hadn't even been offered a phone call home to let my family know where I was and what had happened to me. We were only allowed to shower once a day, at a moment's notice. Most of the time they woke us up in the middle of the night to hold a fresh. Rest of the time we were locked up in this nasty, overcrowded, pitch-black sweatbox. 24/ 7.

Fear and anger started to kick in. Just when I thought my life was changing for the better the street world had me back. I should have listened to my cousin when he said don't go Jamaica. I had to turn wicked just to survive in there. Back to my old ways. Any promise I made to my son about putting down the violence was out the window.

I tried, son. No one can tell you I didn't try to change. I put down the weapons when you was born, I even held back from riding on certain man who violated me back home.

All day and every day I had yardies calling out, "Yo boxer!" 'Bout shower time dis, shower time dat. Then Claws in the cell opposite, the one who said he'd set up the fights for me, would shout "Yo boxer! You ready fi make money? Yuh ah go fight wid da bwoy name Killer." This Claws dude is on my neck, man. Claws had already got inmates to place their bets. I wanted to fuck him up one-on-one if I could get my hands on him.

I wanted to go in the shower and attack whoever wanted to duppy me for no good fucking reason. Inmates were getting killed off inside there. So I didn't take threats lightly.

Being an English boy didn't help. Most of the yard man seemed to think I was the queen's bredrin or something. They kept chatting like the streets of England were paved with gold and kept asking me to 'borrow' them money.

"If I had money, why would I come halfway across the world to get locked up?" I told them.

Some of them were so hard-ears they didn't believe me. They thought I was being selfish, which always led to extra friction. I had people testing my temper and my ego all day every day. Not a single day passed that I didn't want to hurt someone. But if I did the whole jail would turn on me.

I was living my worst nightmare. It was three weeks before I saw a lawyer. We didn't even talk long. All he had to say was that I was looking at three years and that my case was due in court the following week. Is that it? Janet had to send £500 just for this prick in a suit to come and tell me bad news. Chups!

Back in the black hole of my cell, I hadn't been this scared since I was about four. I was that same little boy who slept in the cupboard out of fear when my family were being harassed by the National Front. The fear in me was real. I had threats coming from every angle. Every direction. But it was so dark in there I couldn't see who was making them. Most of the prisoners were there for murder or rape. They were quick to kill. I wasn't scared of them, I was only afraid of allowing my temper to get the better of me. Coz then I would have to kill someone and get life or death row. Then I would never see my son and family again. That was too high a price to pay. Even for my temper.

I found myself praying daily for inner peace. The dreadlock brothers from South London, Screwface and Norm, helped to keep me calm on many occasions, which was funny coz they weren't the calmest people themselves. Certain days they just flipped on other inmates. One of them stabbed an ex crooked cop in front of me. The blood spilled all over my clothes. Screwface said the reason they stabbed the ex cop was coz when he and his brother got locked up they paid him a lot of money to get rid of the evidence of their crimes. The crooked cop ripped them off instead. He took the money and never did jack. His crookedness caught up with him when he got arrested for something else. Then karma licked him and, by no coincidence, he was put in the same cell as the brothers. They weren't about to miss the opportunity to try and kill him.

Jamaican jailhouse was corrupt like whoa! If the price was right, you could get anything you wanted - food, alcohol, bun and cheese, weed, mobile phone, and even your freedom. That weren't nothing special for the way they were treating man on lockdown. That's the least we deserved. They were treating us like some wild, caged, unknown species.

One Sunday the local jailhouse church came down to give praise and worship. It was horrible coz not one of them could sing. While the choir was banging away at their tambourines, a man in another cell was screaming out for his life. Then a few inmates shouted for help. Some inmate had tried to make a small fire in the cell he was in, to warm water for his pot noodles. It weren't a bad idea until the bottle of piping hot water burst. The man was bawling for God but the church and the screws ignored his screams. It was like the church didn't want to get involved. That shit ain't right.

We all started banging on our cell doors and shouting at the church to tell the screws to help. It took another five minutes for the screws to decide to do something and even then they did it slowly. One of them dragged the inmate out by his leg and left him to carry on screaming in pain on the cold concrete ground of the passageway outside the cells. That was some fuckery. All the inmates were shouting. "Put him inna de shower, nah officer!"

A next man who sounded like he was choking with tears screamed,

"God, this is inhumane."

Most of the officers were heartless. Ms Binns was the only bless one, she treated me like a son. But she wasn't on shift that morning.

I started to read a cell mate's Bible. It was strange, coz I never really read the Bible before. Being in a Jamaican prison, I didn't really have nothing to distract me from seeing if it was any good. No TV. No radio. And, of course, no electricity. The only distraction was the screams coming from 'Nam'. But that didn't stop me. Every morning and every night I would read the same prayer and believe every word.

The Lord is my shepherd I shall not want...

For some reason I felt I needed this prayer.

Yea, though I walk through the shadows of death, I shall fear no evil ...

It sounded like it was saying, be prepared for war, you are in hell! But God is with you, have no fear.

Some days the vibe in the jailhouse was live. It was always a random thing. One minute there would be bare arguing from different cells going on. The next minute one of the juveniles would start tapping a beat on the wall. Then a rastaman would jump on the beat with some hardcore vocals. Nothing but true emotion. Everyone could feel the pain and passion in his voice. Dem rastaman had some natural talent in there, it was mad crazy. The only time I heard the jailhouse in complete silence was when the rasta inmate sang one of them righteous songs. Even Claws went silent for those deep lyrics. It was a mad ting.

Behind these prison walls/Doing my paces/Doing my time/I am/Spending my restless nights/Visioning faces/Oh, they all crying/Prison ah nuh bed a roses/The livity it makes me bawl/I wish /ah would come and take us back in time/Cause I swear/That I can be a better man/Yes I swear, if only you could understand/The faith in me shall set me free reflection.
Behind these metal bars/To /ah /ah I'm chanting/Pray for your love divine/I'm oh so sorry I am/Deeply I'm hurting/ The price ordained to be mine/Impossible to see the changes/ That I've made in my life/All they see

is just the boy they left behind/And I swear, that I can be a better man/ Yes I swear, if only you could understand/The faith in me. shall set me free

Don't judge me wrong/Cause now I'm stronger than I was before/I was young and unwise/Didn't you hear my cry/ Impossible to see the change / That I've made in my life/All they see is just the boy I left behind/Cause I swear/I can be a better man/Cause I swear if only you could understand.

That tune had the whole jailhouse in deep thought.

One of the main problems with being on lockdown 24/7 is that the black hole was mashing up my eyesight. Also it was hard to keep track of time. All I knew was that my court date was approaching.

"Officer, what's today's date?"

"8th September, young Henglish," he said. I had to laugh coz it was my birthday and I didn't even know. I spent the rest of the day thinking. Wow! I'm 21 years old. Nuff people told me that the way I was living I wasn't going to make it past my teenage years.

The day before my sentencing the guards decided to raid the cell. They found a mobile phone and claimed it was mine. I told them it weren't mine but they just moved to me anyway. They laid into me with their batons dishing out blows. I snapped and fought back. Big mistake, doh. I got a proper beating after that. At first I was holding my own well, but there were just too many of them.

I might have died in that cell if the owner of the phone, a white Dutch man, hadn't screamed with fear, "Please, leave him alone. It's my phone, not his." Reluctantly, the guards left me alone and turned their attention to the Dutch brother. The officer smiled, grabbed him by the ear and twisted it. That was it. I couldn't believe it. I laughed. Why couldn't they just twist my ear? These coconuts are brainwashed. I stood firm with my swollen body, facing boi-dem as they left the cell. One of them waved his finger at me. "Me know seh ah your phone, " he said. "Next time Henglish, next time."
I gained respect from nuff of the other inmates after that. They saw I wasn't a snitch. And that I had the heart to do what most of them

are shook to do - fight back boi-dem. Where they came from police kill man first, ask questions later. Even that Claws dude stopped bothering me. He even started running jokes with me. This brudder had like three teeth max, but he had jokes for days. He was a bless guy, when he was ready.

Judgment day had come again. I was vex with the man upstairs, he didn't have to let me endure all this pain. God knows I didn't wanna bring them drugs back. Maybe this was God's way of punishing me for all the wrong I did as a young buck on road? Who knows? All I know is that karma is a bi-atch.

Like it or not I had to beg God for mercy coz my lawyer couldn't save me from this one. My back was fully against the wall. I got taken out my cell and cuffed to some next random man who also had his court case. We got escorted outside by police with guns in their waists. The blazing sun blinded me, I hadn't seen daylight for weeks. Still cuffed together we were pushed onto the back of the prison bus and put in a cubicle so small only two skinny men could fit.

In court I was surprised to hear the judge reading a letter on my behalf from my boxing coach in Tottenham. Chris was begging them not to give me a harsh sentence. He wrote that it would damage any chance I had of a career in boxing. He also wrote that I was a young man of good character. I rated Chris for that differently. That's one white man who had my back to the end.

I already pleaded guilty at the last hearing. So today was about how long I was getting. I took full responsibility and refused to snitch on the guys who set me up. The judge told me to stand.

"Robyn Travis, I sentence you to 6 months or J$150,000 for possession, 6 months or J$189,600 for dealing, 6 months or J$224,200 for attempted export, plus 3 months mandatory."

I was pissed but pleased at the same time coz it could have been a straight three years.
"Thank God!" I shouted. Back in the jailhouse the lawyer explained that my three six months sentences ran concurrently. Even better.

God heard my cry. I only had to survive another nine months before I saw my son again. It was going to be hard, but I knew I had to live with it. That same evening I got sentenced. A guard came to the cell, he told me to follow him. He escorted me to an office and handed me the phone.

"Robyn, it's me, mum. Are you okay?"

"I'm cool, mum. You okay? How's my son?"

"Don't worry about me, son, and Rayon is missing you like crazy. Have you been getting the food and clothes we've been sending?"
"No. What food and clothes?

"Aunty Sheryl's mum's been bringing food and clothes down for you from the other side of Jamaica."

"Mum, I beg you, tell her I said 'thanks' but not to waste her time, coz I'm not getting any of that stuff."

"What do you mean? How are you surviving? Whatever you do, stay out of trouble. Oh no, my cred..."

The phone went dead. I didn't have a clue who stole my stuff. It had to be one of the guards. I went back to my cell pissed, enduring my hunger pains, and got on with it. A few days after, I was shipped across Jamaica with nuff other inmates from the jailhouse in Mo' Bay to a Spanish Town prison to start my sentence.

I thought the jailhouse in Mo' Bay was bad, but according to a few hardened criminals in the prison truck Spanish town was "worserer". I was finally able to see daylight, but it was like going back in time two hundred years. The inmates had to use nasty pit toilets with wooden seats, all in a row in the yard. To piss, the inmates had to use bottles hanging on a string from the cell wall. To shower we had to go outside in the yard where five iron pipes were sticking out from a wall. We still had to sleep on the concrete ground and we were still deprived of any real food. There were four inmates in each cell - three on the floor and one in a hammock. We were let out twice a day and had to make do with what little time we had out of lockdown.

I was on a mission. I used that time to exercise. I had to jog on the rocks and stones in the yard in my bare feet coz the guards took my trainers. This prison was crazy. Inmates never solved beef by fighting, they would rather kill. People got killed for fun. It was kill or be killed. I only saw one fist fight in all the time I was there and even that turned into a stone throwing contest. These men were stone throwing specialists. Nuff brudders were getting their heads cut open.

The joke was I was locked up for drugs, but I had never seen so much weed in my life as I saw in that prison. You could smell weed 24/7. I shared a cell with a guy called Scrap Iron, a notorious killer in J.A. who was serving numerous life sentences. We didn't always see eye to eye. He spent most nights talking to his demons. One night Scrappy told me he wanted to kill me. I just looked at him and went to bed. When I woke up the next morning he was standing over me with a screwface. "Yo Zeeks," he called to his bredrin, "the Henglish bwoy nah fraid of me. From now on mek we call him Gangster Golders." He still wanted to kill me. He said he didn't trust people who weren't scared of him sleeping in the same cell.

Scrappy might have been a hitman in his time, but at heart this guy was bless. Certain nights he would get a hot plate and share out two boil' dumplings and some mackerel. Real talk, Scrappy could make a mean boil' dumpling. Other nights we were all awoken by the sound of gunshots on the streets of Spanish Town.

I was never in one place for too long - I swear the feds were trying their best to piss me off. After a couple months I got shipped out to a prison called Richmond Farm. It reminded me of the film *Life* with Eddie Murphy, in which prisoners lived in dormitories, wore funny uniforms and had to work. Then, I was back to Spanish Town sharing with Solomon, Kartel and some next rastaman. Dem man were cool, doh. We cleaned the cell from top to bottom with Dettol every day to kill all the germs and try to kill the cockroaches. In the evenings we rolled dice to kill time. Sleeping on the floor was fucking hard but this cell had the most amazing views, especially at sunrise. Three weeks later I was on the move again. This time to Tamarind Farm for the rest of my sentence. It felt like the storm was nearly over, until the screws put us all on lockdown coz it was hurricane season.

I was missing my son like crazy; I couldn't do it no more, I was dying in there but the one good thing was I had recently got a pen and notebook. I started to write a bunch of my plans, my thoughts and things I wanted to achieve one day. This is what I wrote the night we faced the hurricane.

NOTE FOR MUM:

Sorry for letting you down & putting you through worry & heartache. I just hope you can see that God wanted to get closer to me so he used this time to build up our relationship. Don't think I haven't learnt things coz I have. Just know that I haven't failed yet, Ma. Failure is Fiction, trying is success. It's not what you do, it's what you will become.

I was in the last two months of my time. Everyday had a crazy story. For most of us the madness of life behind bars was too much to bare. I wondered if my past enemies and friends knew I was locked up in Yard. Would they even care? When you're in a negative place it's hard to believe that anyone gives a fuck. Growing up on road I spent most days repping Holly Street, thinking everyone knew how hard we were. In Jamaica no one cared about our rep. They didn't even recognise our struggles.

Jamaica changed me big time. It forced me to dig deep to find all kinds of strength I honestly never knew I had in me. I began to feel like the man upstairs allowed me to experience this hell for a purpose. I've always been a hard-ears yute. Maybe he was trying to teach me something but, coz I don't hear too well, I had to see it for myself. Hard-ears equals harder life.

The poverty in Jamaica sickened me. It hurt me to see people live so hard up and made me think about my own life back home. Although I had it hard to the point where I'd been homeless, nearly died on more than one occasion and spent a lot of my life feeling alone, I realised how lucky I was in many ways. Being in prison in Jamaica gave me a deeper appreciation for life and for humanity. There were days when I was scared and there were days when people needed to be scared of me. The days where I was willing to take out a Goliath, just like Mohammed. I've never had any time for bullies. Then there were the days of unexpected love, like certain man on death row wanting to kill me on Monday and on Tuesday grabbing a hot pot to make me mackerel and dumpling. Jamaican prison was a mad house but it really gave me time to grow.

We had been on 24-hour lockdown for a few days now. I borrowed someone's mobile to check in on Darker. He recently came out of prison himself in England for armed robbery. I let him know I only had two months before man rise again.

"Darker, it's Trav. I soon land. What's been good?"

The line was crackly. It sounded like he said, "Pumas are red."

"What? Can't even hear you, say that again." "POOPS IS DEAD, BRUV. He got shot and killed in Stokey."

"Fuck off, don't lie! Naaah, I saw Poops just before I left."

"I hear you, Trav, but he's gone."

I felt it. Me and Poops were bless from when we met at Daniel House Unit in Stokey. I remembered the last time we met outside the new Peppers and Spice in Dalston.

"Make sure you invite me to your next boxing match," he said. "Hackney needs a real guy to rep the hood."

I got off the phone. Somehow I had to block out this bad news so I could get on with the rest of my bird. Two or three weeks later I was called out of my cell to see the governor. He told me that my sentence was reduced by one month coz my uncle, my Nan's brother, paid a fine. This meant I only had a few weeks to go before this nightmare was over. The night before my release, I was watching airplanes fly over the prison. Yep, tomorrow that's me. That's my freedom. I thanked God for keeping me safe through my ordeal. Then I went to sleep for the last time in a J.A. cell.

I spent the next morning reflecting on all I had experienced during my 'extended holiday'. As tough as my time behind bars was it was harder for my fellow prisoners. Nuff of them were living without hope. I wasn't coming back. They couldn't say the same. On leaving, the feds gave me $3000 (Jamaican), about £30. A large group of prisoners came to the gate to see me off. As I stepped out, I turned and threw the $3000 to them. It nearly caused a riot. The prison guards were angry but couldn't do anything about it.

Two officers escorted me to Kingston, through the gully side of Yard, past some of the worst ghettos. At the airport, I went to the Gents to look at myself in a mirror for the first time in months. I was shocked by the reflection. My hair was as wild as Don King's.

In the departure lounge I met a British-Jamaican woman from Tottenham. She could see I had just come out of prison so she gave me £20.00. When I refused she got real serious with me. She told me she was offended and that I should take the money. So I did. Five minutes later a Jamaican man walked in and said, "Yuh just come outta prison, nah true?"

I put my head down in shame and replied, "Yes." He said he had just been deported from Miami and had done a lot of clothes shopping. "You cyaan go home to your family looking wild like that."
And just like that he gave me some G Unit trainers, a t-shirt and a pair of jeans. I thanked him. I was overwhelmed that complete strangers were showing me love. Maybe it was just good karma - there were certain good deeds I had done when I was locked up. I thanked God and was then escorted by police officers to the plane.

REDEMPTION

When I touched back in England I completely forgot it was winter. As I came through the exit at Gatwick, I saw this little boy running fast and shouting, "Dad, Dad." I thought the yute was running towards another passenger so I ignored him. Then I felt a thump on my leg. It was a crazy moment. That little boy was my son. I tried to play it cool, but I really couldn't register what was going on. I had the craziest sense of deja vu.

"MIND THE GAP! MIND THE GAP!"

Rahtid! I was there kneeling down hugging my three year old son at the airport. The last time I saw my dad he was kneeling down hugging me at the airport. They say that history has a way of repeating itself. I squeezed my son tight. I realised I did what my dad didn't - I came back. I filled the gap.

I picked up my boy, put my arm round his mum and walked outside to my brother's car.

I remembered my promise to divorce the street life. I had put down the guns and knives. I had also put down the weed. All that time I was locked up I never smoked a thing, even though I was surrounded by the highest grade. I made a bigger promise to myself there and then. I will never be away from my son again as long as I live. My brother was parked outside the Arrivals hall. It was good to see him. We gave each other a spud and soon caught up on things.

On the journey home he told me that Smoking Joe tried to fight mum so he had to deal with him. I was mad when I heard this but I had already learnt it wasn't my place to be involving myself. They were in love and mum would always get back with the man regardless of his flaws.

We drove to mum's in London Fields Estate. She was so happy to see me. Her husband stood a few yards behind her. He must have thought I was going to give him the beating he deserved, but I didn't. I just told him, never do it again.

The first few weeks of my return I had revenge in my heart for Brenda's people. I wanted compensation and answers. After a lot of research I got to the bottom of who done what and why. I felt the ones who set me up deserved to get murdered. They panicked when I made threats to do my ting. But I had turned a new chapter, revenge wasn't an option. Deep down I knew I had no one to blame for my actions but myself. If I carried out my feelings of revenge I would only get sent back to prison.

I was made homeless again shortly after my return. I moved back to Hackney to my mum's one bedroom flat in Fields. She didn't want me sleeping on the streets so I slept on her floor instead. One day I spoke with my brother about the future. "What you gonna do with your life, bruv?" he asked.

"Honestly, I dunno. But this shit's getting boring. I just wanna make everything right that went wrong. Y'know, kinda like redemption."

"Why don't you go back to college or something? You're a smart yute when you wanna be." I laughed. This guy didn't understand I wasn't smart academically. God knows how he changed his life around, from big dream chaser to student. Not only was I shocked by his transformation, I was motivated and inspired as well.

After thinking about it for a while, I decided to enrol in an access course in social work at Waltham Forest College. I started college again in September 2007. This time I weren't on no joke business. I didn't want to take education and opportunity for granted no more especially after meeting so many people in prison who couldn't read. I put my head down and started working hard. I always hated school coz I never had the desire to learn what the national curriculum was teaching me, amongst other reasons. But after the things I saw in Jamaica I wanted to learn. I wanted to learn if Great Britain was that great. I was on a mission. Did justice really exist in England?

That thought was my motivation. My mind was opening, I was hungry to learn. My class was full of females who always spoke their minds but there were bare jokes in class. There were only two other boys on the course and a wise African man. I got along with everyone and made a few friends on the way. One day in class I was sitting next to Keisha, one of the older girls. She kept saying, "You really don't remember me, do you?"

"No, why? Where should I know you from?" I said.

She called me out of the classroom and told me she wanted to confess something. We stepped outside.

"Robyn, I know about your past and certain bad things you've done. I've been watching you, waiting to see if you're really that bad person people say you are. But I really can't see it. Anyway, done the long talk, I first met you at Wood Green Crown Court. You were on trial for stabbing my cousin Kaiya."

"Is it?" I told her her what had happened. That day in Totty was mad, I had to ride for my people. She said she understood but assured me her cousin wasn't the type of brother to start trouble.

"Kaiya didn't start the beef in Tottenham that day."

"If you say so, Keisha. Personally I don't believe that. But my past is my past and I can't change it."

If Kaiya didn't start the beef, then who the hell did? I respected Keisha for not judging me like many others did. From then on I knew she was good people.

The academic year was now over. And after a lot of hard work and support I got my first ever qualification - an access diploma in social work. I also completed a course for learning mentors in that same academic year.

My future was becoming clearer. I wanted to work with youths who were involved in these so-called gangs. With my experience I could help one or two young people change their views about 'gang' life. In September 2008 I started to study for a BA degree in Youth Justice and Criminology. I also got a job working as an outreach detached worker in Hackney. It was surreal. I was so used to feeling like a fail-ure that I never thought I could achieve what I did. All I knew was the streets. And now here I was trying to help boys who were involved in the same 'postcode wars' started on my doorstep.

The role I played in this beef wasn't a small one. I felt it was only right that I shared my experiences to save youngers from our argument. I was telling E8 yutes to squash it, it's not their beef. They don't know the true history of why it started. There's a gap missing between the real information and the rumours. Sometimes the youngers listened to the advice I was giving. But then days later it would all kick off again. That shit just made me want to clap them. It hurt to see that my efforts to help them weren't working. I realised that this battle for justice was a lot bigger than me. I didn't do enough to stop my bredrins dying and getting lifed off in prison. With this second chance I'd been given I felt it was my responsibility to warn the youngers of the traps set before them.

They were already mirroring us by going in and out of jail for chasing their dreams. I couldn't tell a younger not to be a dream chaser, but I could show them some of the things that would happen if their dream chasing turned into a nightmare. My main concern was not to see another E8 murder. I was no longer a prisoner to the streets, but the ghosts of my past always followed me. One day I was driving down Holly Street when I saw my old school friend, Con, from Clap-ton. I got out the car and we spudded each other. Then we started to reason. During our chat he brought up a time when I was sixteen years old, and how I rolled on his Springfield boys. I couldn't remem-ber it. He described how me and my Holly Street boys came round his area masked up and how I jumped out of the car and chased him and, when I caught him, started to batter him with a pole.

When he mentioned the pole, I remembered clearly. I explained why we did it: one of their olders had hit one of my youngers. Real talk, we only took it to Con because we couldn't find our target and so any other Springfield boy was a good enough target. "Real talk, fam. I was a young buck dem times. I'm not on that foolish beef ting no more. From the heart, bruv, I'm sorry. We should've got the right person. Me and you were cool in school, and I never should have attacked you for the sake of a younger. It's not like Rocky showed any appreciation for it."

"Cool, bruv," Con replied. "We were all young bucks dem times."

Con added that he heard a rumour that I stabbed a boy called Kaiya back in the day. He also told me that he heard Kaiya didn't start the beef. It was the second time I was hearing this. I needed to put this ghost to rest.

All I could remember was getting out of the car to defend my bredrins who were surrounded by Kaiya's boys. The truth was, I really couldn't say who started it. My thoughts took me right back to my case at Wood Green Crown Court, when Kaiya gave evidence against me. He told the court that he was breaking up a fight between my friend Darker and his friend Half Pint. I started to think, maybe he didn't start the beef. But I couldn't remember, so I put it to the back of my mind. Fuck it. It's not my problem any more.

EDUCATION IS THE KEY

It was 2009 and I was getting on with my new life - boxing, studying and youth work. After my first year at uni a man called Neville organised a trip to Wolverhampton for me to train with a boxing coach for a week. I met Nev by chance when I came back from Jamaica. He had been supporting me along my journey to stay a free man. It was the first Saturday of July and I was getting ready to go to the Midlands. Darker dropped me off at Euston to take the train. At the station I was told my train was cancelled.

I called my children's mother coz I needed the keys for my motorbike parked outside her flat. When I finally got through she said she was at a barbecue across the road from her mum's in Totty. I went mad. She knew I didn't want my children anywhere near there coz earlier that year, an old G from Totty/Wood Green had just come out after a long sentence and tried to stab me. It was hard for me and my ego to hold back and not do some serious damage to him. But I was a changed man, and I wasn't going to let his actions draw out my old behaviour.

When we got there I walked in the house like a mad man. No manners. I didn't say 'hello' to nobody. I just took the keys and walked right back out. As I was leaving, I heard the soft voice of a lady. "Robyn?" I turned to see who it was. A lady walked up and hugged me. "I'm Kaiya's mum," she whispered. "You nearly killed my son."

KAIYA'S MUM'S PART OF THE STORY

This morning I woke up with a jolt, the stark reality that I have to do this. As I am writing I have barely wiped the sleep out of my eyes. Over and over again I have gone over in my head what I would say. I've rehearsed it a thousand times, but I couldn't put pen to paper. You see, the pain is still so raw, so real, even though it's been seven years since Robyn was accused of nearly taking my son's life. Every day since I have been so thankful that God spared my son that night. Every day I say a silent prayer and thank God for his mercies.

I am one of the "lucky mums"; I am not visiting a graveside to see my son. I can still talk to him, laugh with him, hold him and dream of his future. The pain of losing a child would have been too much for me to bear. I would be finished now if my son had lost his life on that night. My heart goes out to all the mothers out there who have lost their children to this infestation of evil in our communities, I write this for you. May we find some peace.

It was a strange night. I was due to fly out to Jamaica the next day for a well-deserved break. I had been ill for some time and my friend had invited me to come over and spend some time with her. My suitcase was packed and my ticket waiting for me at the airport. My two daughters persuaded me that I was doing the right thing, but I was in two minds. I just didn't feel right about leaving them behind. Kaiya was staying with friends in North London and the girls were sorted, but I just had this feeling that I shouldn't go.

In the morning when I woke and checked my mobile, there were fifteen missed calls. Damn, someone was really trying to get hold of me. I called back the number and was told that Kaiya had been stabbed that night outside a club in Tottenham. "Is he alive? Where is he?"

I wasn't interested in what happened I just wanted to see him. I drove to North Middlesex Hospital in a daze, hoping and praying.

There he was, in the middle of the ward, on the right hand side. I stood and stared for a while, holding my breath. He had an oxygen canister next to him, a drip and numerous tubes attached to him. His face was void of any marks but he had bruising to his neck. I later found out that he had a punctured lung and had lost four pints of blood. Everyone came to the hospital - family, friends, all were angry and wanted revenge. Strangely, I didn't feel that way. It still surprises me to this day. I wanted justice. "No, we are going to do the right thing, work with the police and get the person who's done this."

No one else agreed. "Come on, we can't 'llow this to happen," they said. But I was adamant. How could I justify the death or injury of another young person? What kind of mother would I be? I was confused, emotional, and wanted to scream with anger. But something inside me said, No, you must not retaliate.

I found out what happened on that night and who was involved. A boy called Robyn. There was a fight between two girls, my son's friend who was fourteen intervened and was set upon by some boys. Kaiya tried to break it up. As he turned his back to walk away, he felt what seemed like a punch. He had been stabbed.

I went home that day and prayed. I prayed for my son and I prayed for Robyn. On my knees I questioned why I was praying for this boy. Why, Lord? I couldn't and didn't understand, but I cried out for him more than I did for my own son. Little did I know that one day I would find out the reason for my prayers.

During Kaiya's stay in hospital, we never saw the police. I expected them to be interested in my son's attempted murder but no one came. The pressure to retaliate intensified from everyone around me, but I was still determined to do this the right way, through the courts. I wanted the person who had done this brought to justice. I wanted them to pay with their liberty, the way they nearly took my son's liberty. The police were totally useless. CCTV footage was not viewed and was apparently misplaced. In addition the area was never cordoned off for forensics, and now the police didn't have a clue.

Returning home was difficult for Kaiya. The psychological damage was apparent. He found it difficult to accept that he was a victim. It wasn't how he saw himself and I didn't know how to help him. What he found most difficult was that he didn't even see the person who had stabbed him, never saw his face. That was the worst thing for him. He wanted revenge. I spent a lot of time ministering to him, telling him that vengeance wasn't ours but God's. I wasn't sure how much he took in, but it appeared to calm him down.

We found out that Robyn had given himself up to the police. He was charged with the offence and the court date was set. It was apparent from the off that there was poor evidence against him. No witnesses were questioned at the scene.

The trial was at Wood Green Crown Court. I remember walking into court and seeing Robyn Travis for the first time. Oh, how I despised him. My feelings were so raw I wanted him to experience the pain he had inflicted on my child, my son who I loved so dearly. But I remained composed, hoping we would obtain justice. The case lasted three days. I have never been on the side of the prosecution before, but could see that we were losing. Our barrister was a man who appeared to not really care too much. Robyn's barrister was excellent, however, and secured an acquittal. His defence took the approach that this was a black on black motivated attack. Robyn claimed he had acted in self-defence.

Outside the court I completely lost it. I was so shocked at the verdict. How could this happen? He was guilty. How? I shouted at Robyn as he came out of the court. I was devastated. Now I felt guilty that I had somehow failed my son. I went home and tried to forget the whole thing, tried to focus on the fact that I still had a son. However, over the years there would be reminders of what had happened. Flashbacks. Kaiya would take off his top and I would see the stab wound, sending a chill down my spine.

Although things are different now, I am still affected. I never say anything to anyone, but I feel sick when I see the scar or drive through Tottenham High Road where Kaiya was stabbed. I was bitter for a long time, but still thought about when I had prayed for Robyn and how I had cried out for him to be delivered. I hoped he had turned his life around and was out of the street life.

I heard rumours that he had changed his life, apparently studying social work. He even sent a message via a family member who came into contact with him, which I can only describe as divine intervention. He apologised for what he had done. God was now turning him around.

I told Kaiya what I knew but he wasn't interested. He was still very bitter and had pushed the whole thing to the back of his mind. I had mixed emotions. I knew that God had a plan for this young man's life and I continued to lift him up in prayer.

One day, whilst at one of my longest friend's barbecue, I was standing outside watching children play on the bouncy castle when my daughter said, "I know him." I looked around to see a man who I instantly recognised. " So do I, " I said, and walked up to him.

Instantly, the tears began to flow down my face. A mixture of emotions. Here I was in front of the person I had seen in court, who had maimed my son, and yet I was happy, confused, angry. All at once. So many emotions. We spoke for ages. I prayed with him there on the road side and we shared much about what had happened.

I told him that I forgave him for what he had done. I tried to find the right words to express how the whole thing had affected my family. I wanted the right words without condemnation. But it was difficult without demonstrating how I really felt. I invited Robyn to attend my church the following Sunday. However, I knew that I had to tread very carefully as, apart from one of my daughters and my friend, no one knew I had contact with Robyn. I didn't know how everyone would react, but I knew that this meeting was supposed to happen.

Kaiya at this time was away. I felt terrible keeping my secret from him but I didn't know how to tell him about Robyn. It had to be the right timing.

When I eventually told my other children about meeting him, my daughter Casey was very angry and didn't want to know. Despite her opposition, I invited Robyn to my home. It did feel surreal. It also felt natural. All the while checking my emotions. Am I mad? Confused? No, this was supposed to be. Before long my daughter accepted and forgave Robyn.

But there was still Kaiya...(TO BE CONTINUED)

ROBYN'S LETTER TO KAIYA

I have been struggling with my mental for a good few weeks, about a few things in regards to this letter. Will my pride allow me to do this; were you really the victim or the troublemaker that day; how will my letter affect your life?

All of this and more taken into consideration, I have decided to step out on faith and hope you're not a cunt like people have been telling me you are. And, honestly, even if you are, it doesn't matter coz I myself am far from perfect.

Brother Kaiya Truman, I want you to know you never deserved to get stabbed. I wish on a regular I had stayed at home that night and never been a part of any confusion. But we can't turn back the hands of time.

That night on the High Road, I was sitting in the car minding my own business. Next thing I know I saw you and your friends jumping my bredrin Darker. I had to back my boy, which you know is only standard. Without any real thought I jumped out the car. It may seem extreme but we were outnumbered.

Until I finally met you in court and heard your side of the story, I was under the impression that YOU started the beef. In court I heard you say otherwise. You looked genuine in your story, but my mind refused to believe that you and your boys didn't try to rush my boy. The more I think about it, my heart tells me you were innocent. And if my heart is right, I'm sorry for the pain and confusion you had to endure. Wrong is wrong and right is right and even though I've grown up from a young age as a road boy it don't excuse the fact that wrong is wrong. I fucked up. I'm sure you can relate.

I'm not trying to make any excuses for that night, but I have lived a very hard life. All I'm used to is pain and violence. Some of your boys looked like they had shanks on them. I wouldn't of been able to live with myself if I didn't defend my bredrin. I really didn't want to write this, but you deserve to know the truth. I'll admit I came out swinging at whoever swung at me. That was self-defence.

I didn't want to risk my freedom to tell you all this, but my relationship with God has made me send you this letter. I believe my anger of regret over that night is worse than your anger at me. I myself have been stabbed and shot at a million times, and I guess I became a product of my environment. The streets were my parents, the streets were my family and friends. When we're kids we behave like kids. But now we're young men, we should behave responsibly.

You'll never know how hard it's been for me to write you this letter, especially as my bredrin on the day told me that you started the whole thing. Maybe I'm making a BIG mistake in believing that you were innocent that night. But fuck it, my heart tells me you're blessed.

My life has changed now obviously, and I'm not that same hot-head you came in contact with all those years ago. I've finally woken up. I met your cousin Keisha at college, and recently met your mother and little brother - GOOD PEOPLE. They really love you.

You can do whatever you wanna do with this letter - burn it, throw it away or use it against me. Or respect it. It really don't bother me. All I care about is that God blesses you in a special way, and that you can move on with your life and be successful.

Bruv, I wish you all the best when you come out and if you ever want to contact me when you're out, your mum's got my details. But for now, keep your head up, G, heaven's only a mile away.
Peace be with you. (YOU KNOW WHO IT IS)!

KAIYA'S LETTER TO ROBYN

28th August 2009. Kaiya Truman. Approx 6.10pm.
HMP Belmarsh Prison.

Dear Brother Robyn,

On Friday the 28th of August 2009 at exactly 4.49pm I came back to my cell room on A-wing to find a letter in handwriting I didn't recognise. Upon opening the envelope I went straight to the back of the letter to find the person who had sent it wrote, YOU KNOW WHO IT IS. As I began to read the first page I thought somebody was playing a sick joke and I was frustrated and confused.

But as I read further, to my amazement, shock and overwhelming appreciation the letter was sent from a man whose name I would never forget: ROBYN TRAVIS.

Our Lord and father, my brother, has clearly spoken this evening. You have no need to feel your pride has been dented coz you have a heart of courage, warmth and understanding. Your apology, my brother, has been accepted with most gracious of forgiveness. This will also be one of the most difficult of letters I will have to write, but I have trust in our Lord God that he will guide my words to enter the inner depths of your spirit and create the might and power to unite his sons for the kingdom of heaven to rejoice.

Brother Robyn, your letter struck me in a way where my emotions were all over the place. In a way I could not express. I could not eat my dinner and felt I had to put pen to paper to express my thoughts and feelings.

When my mum told me that my cousin, Keisha, went to the same college as you almost a year ago, I thought maybe it's not the same guy. Then my mum said she met you and that you was sorry for what happened, but again it went through one ear and out the other. But to receive a letter was so, so, so unexpected. And your power of expression has resurrected a piece of my pride I thought I had lost forever. Brother Robyn, we may not know each other, but given our circumstances I will share my inner secrets with you, so you can get a sense of feeling of the type of person I am and the love I have for my neighbour.

It has been seven years this month, and not a day goes by where I have not thought about it. Fam, on a level, I had a good night out that evening. I was with my brother and my two bredrins who I refer to as cousins coz we grew up together. I was seventeen and was the second eldest out of the four of us, but since the age of about ten I was always the leader of the pack. When I came out the dance, I saw these two girls fighting. I watched from afar, not really entertaining it, then at the corner of my eye I see Half Pint, the youngest of our group, fourteen at the time, grabbing some youth by the neck and the youth doing the same thing. My brother and I ran over to split it up and, if this is one of your boys, the boy who you said you was with then, I even shook his hand and said, "It's cool, you're bless."

My bro dragged Half Pint to the bus stop and told him to stop hyping. True say he was rolling with the big boys, he must have felt untouchable. Fam, I was the peacemaker, and have been so throughout my life.

After shaking the youth's hand, I headed to the bus stop and some darker skin bruddah with a gold tooth taps me on my back saying, why you starting on one of my youngers? I put my hand on his shoulder and said, "Everything's cool, blud. Then he said, "Don't touch me." Hyping himself I thought, I'm not going to entertain it and I turned my back on him. Turning my back is a lesson I learned the hard way. I will never underestimate anybody again.

The next thing I remember is running. Disorientated and dizzy. I felt like I had been punched in my back, but then I felt this warm liquid flowing down the side of my body. I ended up hiding in some woman's front garden, begging her to let me in. That's when Half Pint said I had been stabbed. I fell to the floor as Half Pint and my brother comforted me and called for an ambulance.

I was in hospital for three days, connected to a drip. They opened up another hole on the same side to clean out the blood . My entire family came to the hospital. Even relatives I had not seen in years. The more family members I saw, the more I cried. My family see me as the ox, able to take on a thousand lions, indestructible. A giant that nobody would even attempt to attack. And there I was, lying in hospital, defenceless, and vulnerable.

I pride myself on the reputation I had and still have. Growing up as a yout man in the hood people know me as a blessed individual full of love and joy. As I have learned over the years people take kindness for weakness and the devil possesses people to tempt them.

The last fight I had was when I was 14 with a guy from my bits of Springfield (Clapton) called Rushman (you might know him). He took kindness for weakness and carried a shank on a regular. Still, I'm old school and we fought like men with our fists and, though I came out on top, the respect we had for each other was mutual. Nobody went hospital and there was no beef on our doorstep. So when the hood heard I'd been stabbed, I could sense their disbelief. I had guy's queuing up for a revenge attack on you, but my mum sat me down and explained that that was exactly what the devil wanted. I decided to 'llow it and let justice prevail. But that didn't happen.

To stand up in that courtroom and open my heart to the events leading to the stabbing was heartbreaking. I think the most distressing part of it all is I never knew who stabbed me, and there you was sitting in the dock. The only face to blame. I remember my mum coming downstairs in the court to ask me if I was carrying a knife. It shocked me coz I could see in her eyes she wasn't sure. As a big man, Brother Robyn, I've never carried a knife nor have I ever stabbed anybody before. Violence is always my last option, and I'm always the first person to squash the beef.

So to answer your question as to whether I was the troublemaker or the victim, I was definitely not the troublemaker. But I prefer not to state I was the victim. Just in the wrong place at the wrong time.

You're right in stating that I'm no angel in terms of my lifestyle, but one of our Lord's commandments that's rubber stamped on my character, is I treat my neighbour as I would want to be treated. No matter what race, sex, religion, job, endz or status. I treat everybody as equals and always try to help the best I can. I'll do anything for anybody and, although there are some ignorant people who see that as a flaw in my personality, I know I was blessed with these qualities to help the children in our community for a brighter future. Brother Robyn, the 'c'-word is pretty strong, but I certainly ain't one of them. I will have words with anyone who says different.

I can fully appreciate your difficulties in becoming a real man and getting sucked into the environment that our roads have become. Thankfully I had my mother who I give the upmost respect to and the fact my mandem were either family or even close friends, and we was more interested in smoking and playing computer and looking girls. Whenever we went out of our way to look for or start any trouble, I managed to stay clear. Peer pressure is a bitch and the devil is a liar, and when you got a not guilty I knew the day would come when I would have to face my demons.

I imagined that one day I would randomly see you on the roads and my pride, emotion and state of mind would get the better of me, and the Lord would lose a son and the devil would gain one.

The code on the street is NO SNITCHING. The fact that I did and you bussed case made me feel like such a wasteman. I had guys from Hackney and Tottenham with guns ready to kill you, but I called it off out of respect for my mum. Looking back, there would have been either you dead or me dead and, yet again, another statistic of how violent our streets have become. Seven years I have had to carry this pain in my heart and dent in my pride, but today you have helped me ease that pain, and I believe the day we meet salvation will surround us and the heavens will be singing the sweetest of songs and the Lord will have favour upon us both.

My plan will be not to say any words but to shake hands and that will speak a million words and we will be at peace with each other and at peace with God.

Brother Robyn, I cannot begin to tell you how much your letter means to me. It's beyond belief you could have easily continued to live your life putting this situation to the back of your mind, but instead you revealed your heart, not knowing how I would react or what the outcome would be. It takes an extremely big man to do what you've done. I have nothing but the greatest respect for you. Seriously. I wear my heart on my sleeve and it seems you do too, so my forgiveness is added with a proposal of friendship. And let's hope we can learn from each other and deter the young children of our future from fighting and warring one another.

The funny thing is that I am currently in prison attending a Sycamore course, which is victim awareness restorative justice. How it works is writing a letter to your victims apologising for your actions. I'm finding it quite difficult to accept the responsibility of my actions as I felt I was acting in self-defence and the person came off worse than I did. We are issued these booklets we have to fill out and one of the questions asked is, if I had ever been a victim and how would I feel if an offender had written to me. And out of nowhere I get your letter.

God is Good. He really can make miracles reality and, without a shadow of a doubt, he works in mysterious ways. I always felt that whoever stabbed me was a coward and one day I would show him what a real man was about. But as for you, you have redeemed and proved yourself to be a warrior, a brave heart and most importantly a child of God. Something I have always been.

Brother Robyn, it's been a privilege to write to you tonight. Your guts and determination has been rewarded with praise. Thank you. I mean that from the core of my soul. You've helped convince me that I should never give up on my Lord and to take pride that I didn't fall under the sword of the devil. You should be mighty proud of yourself.

So take a deep breath and when you breath out it will be a sign of relief and all I'd like you to say wherever you may be as you read this is, GOD IS GREAT. He surely is. Take care, fam, and good luck for your college course and all the best for the future.

Sincerely Mr K. Truman.

Only three weeks 'til my freedom. That's 21 days or 504 hours. Nothing long. Ya get me? Coz freedom is a must. One love.

KAIYA'S MUM'S PART (CONTINUED)

....I spoke to Robyn suggesting that he write to Kaiya as I felt it wasn't my place to take this any further. I know my son and knew his heart. I wanted him to have the opportunity to deal with the situation how it best suited him. Whether it was to forgive Robyn or to vent his anger. He needed closure. Robyn took my advice and wrote. Soon after I received a letter to Robyn from Kaiya. I called Robyn and read it over the phone. The letter made me so proud. The next thing was for them to meet.

I arranged for Robyn to drive down one day when Kaiya visited. Kaiya didn't know who was in the car. When Robyn came out they embraced like brothers.

To this day, there are still family and friends who do not understand how we could have forgiven Robyn. Others are still unaware of the close contact we have. Their feelings are important, but in my eyes not as important as this message getting across. The connection I have with Robyn is one of a mother to her son. I send him texts when my mind runs on him. We sometimes speak for hours, and he calls me 'mum'. I feel blessed to be the one who has the ability to embrace a young man who needed to be released.

Robyn, I thank God for your life. May all your dreams be manifested. Yes, we released you by our forgiveness, but you also released us by your determination to change. Well done, son. My heart grieves for young people - the maiming and killing. Not just black on black, although this is a huge part of it. Educate yourselves, stand up and be counted and be free.

WE need YOU. If you can't read get audio education. Feed your mind with positive not negative influences. It is not impossible to change.

I'm sorry for what we have done to you. If my generation had been more focused on our children maybe we wouldn't be where we are now. Forgive us.

Finally, to all the young people who feed into 'gang' culture, there are organisations which will support you to come out of it. Why live the way you are? You are somebody. Be who you were born to be. This is my prayer for you.

REVELATIONS THE DREAM

I was so stressed out one afternoon in January 2011, that I fell into a sudden deep sleep. I started to have this dream - so real that you think you're wide awake. In the dream I was running down Queens-bridge Road, Hackney, near my old yard in Holly Street when I bumped into Jadie. What confused me is that I thought he was dead. Jadie called me over and gave me a high-five, followed by a hug, and said, "Wah gwarn."

"Nothing," I said, "I'm just 'ere trying to behave myself these days. I'm not the same guy, but I am if you get me."

"Yeah, I know, Rob. I've been hearing about you still."

I couldn't help but notice that he had spots of blood on his face. His afro high-top was still neat, but bloody, and his leather Avirex jacket also had spots of blood on it. It was then that I realised that he was half-dead.

"So Rob, you're not on the roads again, bruv," he said.

"Nah, I'm working. I drive disabled children to school and back. And I'm a father now. I got a child of my own."

"Cool. I'm really happy to hear that, Rob."

Whilst Jadie was trying to catch up with me his phone wouldn't stop ringing. He finally answered it and snapped at the person on the other end.

"Look, I'm chattin to my bredrin I ain't seen in time. Wait, I'll be there in a minute."

He hung up, looked at me and smiled.

"Rob, I gotta keep it moving. These people won't stop ringing my phone. I gotta get down to Fields."

I smiled back.

"You gotta run down Fields? That's just across the road. You say it like it's far, Holly Street/Fields same ting."

There was an awkward pause and for the first time in my life I saw Jadie speechless with a frozen facial expression. He paused for a bit and with a confused look on his face said, "Yeah Rob, you're right. It's silly innit. But it's too late now."

He told me to keep up staying off the streets and gave me another high-five and hug. Then he vanished into thin air.

I woke up from the dream stunned. The constant reminder of how stupid this war was, and many other postcode wars like it, started to haunt me. The distance between Holly Street and London Fields is about 400 metres, a distance Usain Bolt could run in less than a minute.

It took me ages to get out of bed after that dream. My body wouldn't move, and I was pacing for breath. I was so confused about what the dream was all about. Over the next few days I asked a few people to tell me if this dream was some kind of sign but no one could give me an answer.

I got stabbed at fourteen years old and nearly died as a result of this foolish Holly Street vs London Fields postcode beef. Jadie was just like me, but he lived on the London Fields side of E8. He had the same keeping it real/ ride or die mentality as I did. Sadly for him, when Holly Street and Square came for him with guns, he didn't respect them enough to run. Jadie was shot fatally. Rest in paradise, J.

Somehow I survived and turned my life around. He didn't get to tell his story, but his life and death affected so many people.

A few days after my dream, I went to the library to research on some dates in the Hackney Gazette archives to help me write this book accurately. That's when I realised that Jadie was shot and died on 9th June 2003. I got stabbed and nearly died on the 9th of June 2000. Coincidence or a sign? You decide.

EYE FOR AN EYE, TOOTH FOR A TOOTH

I spoke with one of my friends from Tottenham recently. I told him I knew the guy who killed his brother, and that he was coming out of prison soon. My friend nodded his head and said, "Yeah Rob, I'm counting the days."

I then told my friend that when I was going on wild on these streets, my brother called me aside and said, "Robyn, you're my little brother and I love you. But if anyone ever kills me, don't kill in my honour." I laughed at what my brother said and replied, "You're a mad man. I'm killing the same night."

"No, Rob. When I die you won't know where I'll be. For all you know, it might be a place a lot better than this. And I'd hate to be in that better place knowing you're serving a life sentence coz of my absence."

When my brother said that, the words of the reggae song by Buju Banton rang out in my head:

MURDERER! Blood is on your shoulder Kill I today, you cannot kill I tomorrow.

After I shared that story with my friend from Tottenham he gave me a firm handshake and said, "Rob, no one's ever put it in that way before."

"Forget pride or what the streets say," I told him. "I would personally

respect you if you don't throw away your life by retaliating."
I know that those real words opened his eyes to a different understanding.

Sleep well to all of those who lost their lives to this prisoner to the streets mentality and, S.I.P (Serve in Peace) to all of those who are doing life sentences for their murders. Coz we're not our behaviours and we're not a reflection of the crimes that we've committed, and we're not our emotions. We weren't born gangsters, murderers or drug dealers, thieves, or road-boys repping the streets. We learned our prisoner to the streets behaviour.

Your endz ain't badder than anywhere else. There are no winners in war. If you kill ten of my friends and I kill just one of yours, we both lose. The simple truth is, you can't measure a life by numbers. The sad truth is, everyone who rides for their endz is losing. When we war and kill each other, we're the only ones loosing. Some say that the system put drugs and guns in our areas to keep us down and at war. Others say that this is just a conspiracy. Either way, we can't blame anyone else for the part we play in the madness. We complain when they send us to prison to do time but yet we're already prisoners in our own minds. If we do end up in their prison, then I know when we come out, it's almost impossible for us to change our lives coz we're stained with memories of our past behaviours. We're being controlled and we're so blind with hating each other or looking for street fame that we miss the obvious trap that's been set for us. When are we going to wake up and stop wasting time with these little street wars? Coz we're losing the bigger war. Freedom.

This book was never meant to be a judgment. I'm not saying that because I've written this book I'm some kind of hero or better than anyone else. All I'm saying is that people watch our actions so we have to be the best example we can be. We're giving way too much attention to glorifying this street mentality that we're dimming the hope for our children. If it means squashing the beef, changing a mentality, putting down our egos, so our children can walk the streets freely and not be afraid of their own, then I'm all for it.

MIND THE GAP, MY BROTHERS!

POETS' CORNER

I gave people a space to express their thoughts in relation to the themes in this book. On the following pages are a few poems that were selected to be printed.

STREET PRISONER

From the blessing of birth and the liberation after 9 months of incubation into Western civilisation from the warmth and safety of the womb.

Not aware of your impending doom as a male to the 'system' and the lure of the streets and the spoiled fruits that it reaps.

You had so many dreams and aspirations for your future, but life is a great teacher and as you grew older your ambitions were snatched from you one by one.

Fragmented from society, based on your notoriety, your parents left you no legacy and poverty seemed to surround you like flies on a dead body.

Already considered a 'state enemy' before your conception coupled with no direction from absent husbands who leave behind abandoned children with no protection.

But in the streets you are accepted and represented, there's a small partition where you can fit in, demanding your lost respect and chasing currency in a 'dog eat dog' world.

In the process you forgot that you are your 'brother's keeper,' instead you have become your brother's reaper.

Collecting the souls of each other and leaving behind weeping mothers, as you limit travel borders and territorially mark street roamers.

Upholding postcodes instead of patrolling roads in defence of your brothers and sisters in your community.

This selfish mentality is causing the death of our Afrikan family; we have become an easy target for our enemy.

Who taught you to hate yourself? In the 50's racism used to chase our grandparents down in the streets, now in 2016 you spill each other's blood on the same cold concrete.

Restricting one another to area codes which are neighbours, while minimalising your brother's freedom and worsening our collective condition.

You now play hide and seek in the streets with the police in a game of mouse trap. Drugs and guns are pushed into our communities to distract you from unity with your brothers.

Together we are a mighty army, but you disarm us with your misguided actions, we all want the same thing, freedom of expression.

But the oppression you feel is from the 'establishment' who patrol your 'endz' with their CCTVs and take away all of our civil liberties. We don't want to read anymore 'black on black' eulogies, or hear anymore incarcerated apologies.

We want the continuity of our race, we are a misplaced people. Stop this self-hate; it is time to participate in repairing the damages to our people and fighting to eradicate all evil.

Take back your position as the 'heads' and 'warriors' of our Nation, You are the true fathers of civilisation. Instead of being a prisoner to the streets and this western system.

By Leafy Bee

THROUGH THE EYES OF A CHILD

A little boy alone on the streets, no father to guide him, no mother to protect him, no parents to love him.

He cries, he rebels, he is scared, he is hurt and feels pain.

A confused immature male lost in the wilderness, neglected by his bloodline, rejected by many in his environment.

He cries, he rebels, he is scared, he is hurt and feels pain.

A teenager angered by his many attempts to be heard and understood, silently battling with his frustrations.

He cries, he rebels, he is scared, he is hurt and feels pain.

A young man unaware of his actions oblivious to consequences he may face unknowledged, un-informed he has no wisdom.

He cries, he rebels, he is scared, he is hurt, and feels pain.

This *person* has feelings, is *somebody*, has lost a loved one or is emotionally distraught.

He will cry he will rebel.

HE IS SCARED, HE IS HURT, AND HE FEELS PAIN.

Everything we go through in life there is a reason *for it* and *behind it*.

Everything they do, is a reflection of you.

DON'T TURN A BLIND EYE, LISTEN, ADVISE, ENCOURAGE.

By Veronica Henriques

THE PAIN IN MY HEART

I'm writing this poem in deep unrest, but I am determined to keep going until I fulfil my quest.

I'm writing to you! The unrestrained one that holds the blame, So that you can be aware of my anguish and pain.

Who gave you the right to take my son's life? That pain is worst than cutting me with a two edge knife.

He was mine for me to love and care for,
Coz of you, now my first-born is no longer here.

The disrespect you have concerning life is wrong,
your generation have no idea how to carry on

It's about time that you all use your senses and shape up. My son waited far too long and ran out of luck.

I lost my son and that was so unfair.
Whether you meant it or not, is neither here nor there.

One thing though, you still have your life. Your mum can watch you go to bed each and every night.

I can't picture you, coz I don't know who you are.
But to me that feels like an added scar.

Every day the pain still hurts! Truly I simply can't cope.
My neck feels like it is tied tight with a rope!

By Zelda Gunzell

MAMA CAN'T RAISE NO MAN
By Robyn Travis

MAMMA CAN'T RAISE NO MAN

ROBYN TRAVIS

An eye-opening, laugh-out-loud funny, debut novel
which explores ideas around black masculinity in today's
society.